Jessica had no time for affected idlers of Leandro Volpi's type. Her world revolved around her work, and she was not out to be sidetracked by the casual interest of a mere playboy. But Leandro was very determined. . .

CHALLENGE

BY

SOPHIE WESTON

MILLS & BOON LIMITED
15-16 BROOK'S MEWS
LONDON W1A 1DR

*First published in Great Britain 1987
by Mills & Boon Limited*

© Sophie Weston 1987

*Australian copyright 1987
Philippine copyright 1987
This edition 1987*

ISBN 0 263 75693 9

*Set in Monotype Times 10.5 on 10.9 pt.
01-0687-69214*

*Typeset in Great Britain by
Associated Publishing Services
Printed and bound in Great Britain by
Collins, Glasgow*

CHAPTER ONE

'BUT what's he like?' Sue demanded impatiently.

Jessica Shelburne negotiated the long low car carefully out of the approach road to Genoa airport before answering.

'Prince Giorgio?' she asked, having accomplished this feat with the aristocratic paintwork unblemished, at which she expelled a sigh of relief. 'Oh, very charming, as you might expect. Though he wants his money's worth out of us, as you'll find.'

Sue snorted. 'Giorgio di Stefano is sixty years old and highly unattractive into the bargain. What's more I've already met him—though you're pretending to have forgotten the fact. I mean the nephew.' She threw Jessica's profile a quick look and gave a mock-languorous sigh. 'The devastating Leandro.'

'Oh, the Body Beautiful.' Jessica's answer was absent-minded. She glanced in her wing mirror as she swung the borrowed car to the left on to the *autostrada*. Then, relaxing, she answered the question, her tones tinged with mischief. 'He's very much as advertised. Tall. Tanned. Gorgeous. Doesn't do a stroke of work. . .'

Sue laughed. 'When you look like he does, who needs to do a stroke of work?'

'When you live like Leandro Volpi, just about anyone,' Jessica said drily.

'Oh, don't be sour, Jess,' protested Sue. 'Just because you're a workaholic, it doesn't mean the rest of the world has to be the same.'

'You and Leandro are clearly soulmates,' observed Jessica. 'He's been telling me the same thing every day for the last fortnight.'

Her assistant grinned. She knew her employer. 'Been lecturing him, Jess?'

Jessica laughed aloud. 'I wouldn't even try. He's a man who knows what he wants and how to get it. Honest toil doesn't come into the equation.'

'And what about lectures from his uncle's employees? Where do they figure?' murmured Sue.

'On the list of occasional amusements.' There was a pause, then Jessica said with something of a snap, 'Leandro Volpi finds me highly entertaining.'

'Ah,' said Sue, not entirely sure of the right response.

She knew that Jessica had wanted the assignment. She had worked hard for it, harder even than her usual ten-hour day. Prince Giorgio had been impressed by her preliminary ideas; that was why he had asked her out to Italy to look at the site and meet some of the other people involved in the project. Andrew Lamont, her partner in architectural practice, had teased Jessica about her 'holiday' on Prince Giorgio's luxury yacht, but in truth neither he nor anyone else in Shelburne and Lamont believed that Jessica would do anything other than work during her visit.

'She'll get annoyed if they try to make her enjoy herself,' Andrew had said with relish to Sue. He was a bit afraid of Jessica, who was the driving force in their partnership.

Sue had not agreed with him. For one thing, she was Jessica's secretary, not Andrew's, and loyalty kept her silent. For another, she had known Jessica long enough to realise that she only worked so hard because she genuinely enjoyed it. She was nothing like the killjoy that Andrew liked to pretend.

So Sue had been more surprised than Andrew when Jessica had returned from that first visit to the boat clearly in two minds about whether to return. Andrew had laughed and said they had probably tried to take Jessica windsurfing, but Sue had detected a reluctance in her employer which she really did not think was due to the frivolity of shipboard life. She had waited for Jessica to tell her what was wrong, but Jessica had kept her own counsel and in the end had gone back to the yacht as planned.

Now, looking at Jessica's set face, Sue began to wonder whether the reluctance had anything to do with the presence on board of Leandro Volpi.

Unaware of Sue's speculation, Jessica was concentrating on her driving. She needed to concentrate; she was afraid of the great car that Leandro had insisted on lending her. Pride, of course, would not permit her to admit that to him, so she had accepted the loan gracefully.

But it was not just the car. She was afraid of the road, which was a brilliant feat of engineering, alternately crossing gorges on stilts or plunging into tunnels through the hillsides. The adjustment every few mintues from blackness to glaring sunshine made Jessica stiff with tension. She realised she was hunching over the steering wheel and made a conscious effort to relax before Sue noticed.

A car shot past. It was travelling fast, too fast, and Jessica jumped as it flickered across the corner of her vision. This was ridiculous, she told herself. She was travelling at a moderate speed herself; it was pointless to be frightened by the speed of those drivers whizzing past in her left wing-mirror.

She set her teeth. Think about something else, she urged herself, think about work, think about an ordinary journey to the office.

Her lips twitched involuntarily. Shelburne and Lamont had an exquisitely decorated but small set of offices in a Regency house behind the British Museum. Jessica seldom took her car to the office because of the traffic and the difficulty of parking, so the journey to work usually consisted of a short period of determined endurance on the underground and then a brisk walk.

'I don't know how you can bear it,' Andrew Lamont said to her. He loved his car and was quite prepared to sit in traffic jams for over an hour in order to travel to work in that fashion.

Jessica laughed at him. 'One of the reasons I live in Holland Park is so that I can use public transport,' she told him. 'If I were prepared to drive I'd live somewhere leafier and much cheaper.'

Andrew doubted that. Jessica's flat was a stylish studio, very high, with skylights that captured light like a prism. It was elegantly decorated and very comfortable, but she was, as he pointed out, hardly ever there. Jessica had rapidly become the primary international specialist in the firm, and she spent much of her life in hotel rooms as a result.

'But it's so inconvenient to have to go home to pick up the car if you're going to a party or something,' Andrew protested.

Jessica gave a choke of laughter. 'Exactly, Andrew,' she said approvingly. 'An excellent excuse not to go.'

He sniffed, unamused. 'You're unnatural!'

'Because I do what I like?' she asked, cocking an eyebrow at him.

'Because you don't like anything but work!'

Another car flared past, and Jessica winced. Her palms were damp on the steering wheel. She looked sideways to see whether Sue was nervous, but Sue, bless her, appeared to be asleep.

Jessica bit her lip and tried to concentrate on her thoughts.

Was it true that she liked nothing but work? She reviewed her life. When she was not travelling, she was usually in the office by eight o'clock, but that was only sensible. That way you avoided travelling with the crowds in the rush-hour tube trains.

She recalled, sharply and unwillingly, her first encounter with Leandro Volpi. That had been one of the rare mornings when she was late and had arrived hot and dishevelled from her brush with London's commuters.

The moment she hurried through the door, she had been aware of the tall man with Prince Giorgio. He was casually dressed, wearing an open-necked shirt and dark glasses, and patently amused. Jessica distrusted the amusement and she hated the glasses on sight.

And Leandro, she was fairly sure, had taken the measure of her reaction at once. It had increased his amusement. In fact, that amusement was the only possible justification for all that had followed.

Unconsciously, Jessica sighed. What was Sue going to make of it all? So far Jessica had not confessed to anyone that Leandro Volpi, for whatever dubious motives, had decided to entertain himself by pursuing her. Now, however, Sue would see it for herself. She could hardly avoid seeing it.

Jessica sighed again, slowing into a curve. She did not, she acknowledged, know what Leandro was up to. She had not known, right from that first day.

He had taken no part at all in her discussions with Prince Giorgio. He had sat there looking indifferent while they discussed outline specifications and when, on one occasion, his uncle had asked his opinion, he had shrugged comprehensively.

When the visitors had left, Jessica had been oddly relieved. She had not liked the way Leandro Volpi kissed her hand with what she was perfectly aware was outdated ceremony. But she had not expected to see him again. . .

To her astonishment he had materialised on her doorstep that evening. She returned from work to her quiet

mews to discover him sitting cheerfully on a bollard at
the mews entrance swinging his feet and still wearing his
sunglasses, although it was nine o'clock at night.

'Good evening,' Jessica said frostily. 'Are you staying
in this area, Signor Volpi?'

It was the first of many opportunities, she was to discover, which she gave him to tease her.

He laughed. 'So far, I am not so fortunate.' And gave
a theatrical Latin lover's sigh which made her glare at
him, even while she blushed. He hopped off his bollard and
took her portfolio case from her. 'No, I am dining
here. With you.'

Jessica was outraged. 'I am not cooking you dinner,'
she said forthrightly, forgetting the man was the nephew
of a valued prospective client.

'Of course not,' he soothed with a kindness which set
her teeth on edge. 'We will go out to dinner. I have
booked a table at a restaurant run by a friend of mine
just a few streets away.' He took her key, which she had
just extracted from her handbag, and went to her front
door. 'This house, is it not? Charming.'

He stood back to allow her to precede him. In a daze—
a state of affairs which he seemed to bring about all too
easily, as she was to find out—Jessica did so.

'You have time,' he told her graciously, 'for a shower
before you change. I did not know when you would be
home, so I gave no time. Carlo will hold our table for
us.'

Jessica stared at him for a moment, torn between
annoyance and a sneaking amusement. She had intended
to work on the project she was completing before Prince
Giorgio's assignment, and had come home wanting a
bath and a piece of toast before she went back to work.
Now, however, she hesitated.

There was no hesitation in Leandro. He was wandering round her studio looking with interest at the books
and prints. He looked up.

'Well, go on,' he said gently. 'I'm hungry, even if you aren't.'

If he had tried to persuade her she would not have gone. At the slightly impatient rebuke, however, Jessica capitulated.

'Do you know something? You're mad,' she informed him, going.

She was to tell him much the same thing later.

'What do you normally do in the evenings?' he asked, when she thanked him for the unexpected treat.

Jessica shrugged. 'What does anyone do? I read. I listen to music quite often. I——'

Leandro flung up a hand. 'I know. Don't tell me. You work.'

Jessica eyed him coldly. 'You disapprove?'

He grinned. 'Naturally. Work is the only rival a man cannot compete with.'

Jessica gave a choke of laughter, quickly suppressed, and primmed her mouth. 'In my case, you hardly need to compete.'

'No?' He leaned forward, looking interested. 'You have already succumbed to my manly charm?'

Jessica was horrified and it showed. 'Of course not. What on earth have I said?'

Leandro sat back again in his chair, shaking his head.

'You are too sensitive, *cara*,' he said. 'Too sensitive and too serious. There is more to life than work, you know.'

He paused. There was a pregnant silence. Jessica held on to her temper and met his eyes levelly. They were, she found, dancing.

It was irresistible. In spite of her annoyance at his teasing, she felt an unwilling laugh rise.

'Oh, you're impossible,' she said at last, smiling. 'If I'm too serious, you're never serious at all. It makes you very irritating.'

He flicked her cheek with long, careless fingers.

'Alas, I know it. You are very charming when you are irritated, though.'

Jessica sniffed. 'I think it most unchivalrous of you to bait me as you do. You may be surprised to hear it, but I'm normally held to be very even-tempered.'

'I am not at all surprised,' Leandro said calmly. 'I have very little doubt that normally you get your own way all the time.'

Just for an instant her eyes flashed, then she caught herself and flung up a hand in surrender.

'All right, all right, I give in!' She lowered her hand and tried for a conciliatory tone. 'I'm a terrible managing woman and you don't know what to do with me.'

Leandro gave a chuckle. 'I know exactly what to do with you, *cara* Jessica, as you will discover one day.' He eyed her expectantly. Jessica disappointed him, holding on to her blank expression with determination. He shrugged his shoulders, though his eyes twinkled. 'But for the moment we will not speak of it.'

Jessica refused to be drawn. She gave him a bland smile, which totally belied her inner wariness. Leandro Volpi had a reputation with women which, she judged from her brief acquaintance with him, he fully deserved.

Jessica half expected Leandro to make a heavy pass at her when he escorted her back to her apartment that night. If he had done so, she would not have seen him again. But he was too clever for her.

As she stood looking at him cautiously, he gave her that devastating lopsided grin.

'We will, I hope, see more of each other in the future,' he murmured, shaking her hand firmly. 'It has been very stimulating.'

And he walked away without so much as kissing her goodnight, to Jessica's amazement and unconfessed disappointment. It was almost like a challenege.

Sexual challenges were problems she needed like a hole in the head, she told him in exasperation when he rang her the next day. He laughed and soothed her.

'Why so excited, *cara?* What can I do to you?' he asked, reasonably enough.

And the trouble was that she did not know what he could do to her. She did not really doubt her own ability to keep things cool if he was bent on seducing her. The trouble was that she was not sure whether that was his object or not. Sometimes it seemed as if he was absolutely determined on it; sometimes it seemed as if it was all a game to him.

The other trouble, Jessica admitted to herself, was her own lack of experience, particularly with the practised charmers of Leandro Volpi's type. For her own reasons she had avoided involvement with men. There had been one devastatingly hurtful but fortunately brief encounter, after which she had decided that work was more rewarding. So she was peculiarly unfitted to handle Leandro's sophisticated teasing.

After her first sojourn on the yacht she had very nearly decided to turn the project down, so unfitted was she. After talks with Andrew, and at Sue's evident astonishment, however, she had decided that she owed it not only to the partnership, but also to her self-respect, to carry the thing through. But she had not wanted to return to the yacht, more than she would have believed possible.

It was extraordinary. She had never been so conscious of a man—or so wary of one. Not even when she was young and in love for the first time had she felt so utterly helpless. None of it was made any easier, of course, by the dark suspicion that for Leandro the whole business was simply a way of whiling away otherwise boring hours while he lazed about his uncle's yacht.

Jessica bit her lip in recollection. It had been there from the moment she had come on board, like a palpable presence. She had become aware of it from the moment the stewardess, sighing romantically, had told her that she would be dining *à deux* every night with the *signor*— who was, of course, so glamorous.

Faintly amused, Jessica had replied neutrally. She had not, however, remained amused. For one thing, she was not used to having her private life as comprehensively monitored as the crew of Prince Giorgio's yacht favoured. For another, there had been a general air of expectation which had made her both angry and super- stitiously uneasy. There had been no disguising the happy assumption of the entire cabin crew that the star- lit nights, the voluptuous warmth of the days, the abundant hospitality of her absent host and the innate seductiveness of Leandro's presence would all conspire to tip their guest headlong into love with that famed breaker of hearts. They had all been generously pleased at the prospect.

Jessica was not so sure that Leandro himself shared this romantic view. He had paid her extravagant com- pliments, certainly, and pantomimed strong attraction. But even when he was carrying her stiff fingers to his lips, or gazing into her indignant eyes, there had always been a tell-tale twitch at the corner of his mouth, no matter how limpid the eloquent eyes, or how beguilingly husky the voice. Jessica was fairly certain that Leandro had been hugely enjoying himself—partly at playing up to the romantic expectations of the crew, partly at her own disapproval.

The signs were coming up for Portofino, and Jessica followed them carefully, holding the big car at a low speed. She felt as if she were trying to restrain a tiger. Beside her Sue stirred.

They reached the area where the di Stefano cars were normally left. A uniformed man was waiting for them, Sue saw. Jessica got out of the Lamborghini rather stiffly and handed him the keys. He took Sue's cases and put them on a small trolley before wheeling them down to the port, and within mintues they were on the launch, headed for the big yacht in the bay.

'How was your journey, *signorina*? Did you enjoy the car?'

Sue nodded. Jessica, frowning slightly, did not seem to hear. The uniformed sailor cast Miss Shelburne a look of respect.

'It is a great honour. The *signor* is very careful of his car. I,' this was clearly a deeply felt grievance, 'am not allowed to drive it, though I use all the other cars, including the Prince's Porsche.'

Sue nodded again, impressed. She wondered whether Jessica knew and concluded, from her abstracted expression, that at the moment at least she would not be interested. Sue began to wonder, for the first time, exactly what was the relationship between her hard-working employer and Leandro Volpi, who, from what Jessica had said, she gathered was more or less a professional idler.

She wondered even more when they arrived and Leandro came to meet them, tanned and smiling, muscles rippling unashamedly in his naked shoulders as he bent to reach for Jessica.

'*Carissima!*' His voice was tender, even affectionate, and just a trifle too husky to be sincere.

Sue cast him a look of respect. Jessica was clearly being teased by an expert and it looked as if, for once in her self-possessed life, she did not know how to handle it. She seemed flustered and faintly cross as he raised her hand to his lips.

The crewmen, waiting to unload the luggage, were impassive.

'And Miss York.' Leandro turned to Sue with a friendly smile quite unlike the elaborate charm he had used on Jessica. 'I hope you had a good journey.'

'Ex—excellent, thank you,' stammered Sue.

Even when he was not sighing meltingly over a lady's hand, Leandro Volpi was, she discerned, dynamite. She encountered a look of burning reproach from Jessica.

The smile crinkled the corners of his eyes, which were wide and golden, fringed by long curling lashes that many a professional beauty might have envied. As he handed her aboard, smiling, Sue had the distinct impression that he was inviting her to share his amusement at Jessica's discomposure, as that lady tugged her hat into a more aggressive angle and glared at him.

But all he said was, 'Nevertheless, you must rest, if you would like to do so. Graziella will take you to your cabin. She will bring you whatever you require—food, a drink, coffee; even English tea if you are like Jessica and insist on drinking that abomination.'

Sue looked uncertainly at her employer. There was a lot of work to be done, she knew, and not a great deal of time in which to do it. Maybe it would be better if they started at once.

Leandro intercepted that look and interpreted it accurately.

'Surely,' he drawled, though there was an unexpectedly steely note in his voice, 'Jessica will not grudge you a rest after travelling for. . . what? Six hours?'

'Nearer eight,' snapped Jessica, who knew exactly where Sue lived in the depths of the Berkshire countryside, since she was a frequent and welcome visitor in the York family home. 'And I was about to suggest that she took a siesta, as a matter of fact. It was very hot in Genoa and the air-conditioning in you car either turns it into an iceberg or doesn't work at all.'

He raised golden eyebrows, mocking her. 'And you are *objecting*?' He managed to sound incredulous. 'But I thought you were only comfortable at arctic temperatures. I will have the thermostat changed before you travel in it again. If you're sure.'

'Thank you,' said Jessica. 'I see no need to travel in it again, however.'

He laughed, shaking his head at her. 'What is this need? It will be my pleasure to drive you.'

And he, presumably, would take the monster at the speed for which it was designed, thought Jessica, suppressing a shudder; she was not proud of her phobia about speed. Which was something even Sue did not know, and she would die rather than admit it to Leandro Volpi. She registered a vow that she would never, under any circumstances, accept an invitation to drive with him.

Sue was being escorted to her cabin by an attentive stewardess, and adjured by Leandro to ignore any demands Jessica might make and rest for as long as she wanted.

When she had gone, the crew disappeared as if melted by the afternoon sun. It was done tactfully, and the very tact added fuel to Jessica's fury.

'You never give up, do you, Leandro?' she said coldly.

The golden eyes which were so eloquent when not hidden by the habitual dark glasses turned to her questioningly. 'I?'

'Don't sound so innocent! You know what I'm talking about.'

His grin became lopsided. '*I* do, certainly. I sometimes wonder whether you have realised. You will, though.'

Jessica looked eloquently round at the deserted deck. She was well aware that the twenty-man complement of the yacht regarded her prickly relationship with Leandro as a source of huge entertainment. It galled her, but she was fairly certain that it only added to his own enjoyment of the situation. She was not, therefore, alarmed by the sensuous, caressing note that he had permitted to invade his voice. Leandro, she was fairly certain, was being wholly mischievous.

She gave him her sweetest smile. 'Is that a threat or a promise, *signor*?'

The golden lashes flickered. 'Let us call it a forecast,' Leandro said smoothly.

'Oh, like the weather?' Eyes wide, Jessica nodded. She let the pause draw out before adding innocently, 'Of course, they're often wrong, aren't they?'

He was laughing. 'Their timing is sometimes a little erratic,' he agreed. He paused, as she had done. The golden eyes became smoky, even ardent. '*My* timing, on the other hand is impeccable.'

Jessica was startled into a choke of laughter, quickly suppressed. She would not give him the satisfaction, she told herself—almost certainly in vain, because he was looking complacent.

'I suppose you have often been told so?' she enquired in a strangled voice.

'Frequently. Not, of course,' he added, 'that I needed to be told. With some people these things come naturally,' he assured her in all solemnity.

Jessica strove with herself. 'I congratulate you,' she said at last.

He gave her another of his slow smiles. She privately thought of it as his satisfied tiger look.

'Talents are nothing if they are not shared,' he told her largely.

Jessica gave up the unequal struggle against mirth. When she had stopped gasping with laughter she discovered Leandro looking at her with a kindly expression.

'That is better. Now you are not so tense. Now you will go and sunbathe on the foredeck and snooze until it is time for cocktails.'

But this was too much.

'Oh no, I won't,' said Jessica. 'I'm a working girl, not a lounge lizard. I have plans that need looking at.'

Leandro appeared pained. 'You think I am a lounge lizard, beautiful Jessica?' His voice took on that spurious, caressing note again. 'Even though I, too, have plans?'

'I'm sure you have,' she agreed drily. 'But I doubt if they're the sort you plot out on graph paper and accompany with costings.'

He did not answer her at once. Eyes dancing, he leaned back against the side of the boat, one tanned leg bent, bracing him, while he flung back his head to gaze mournfully at the cloudless sky.

Jessica did him the justice to acquit him of adopting the pose deliberately. He was, after all, quite accustomed to his own magnificent physique. In fact, he seemed uncharacteristically modest about it, even unaware. Of course, he must be accustomed to being admired. He did not need to pose to attract attention.

But it was a stance which threw into relief the beautifully proportioned muscular frame, the jutting shoulders that gleamed like oiled gold, the fine profile, the brown curling hair bleached in streaks by long hours of exposure to the Mediterranean sun. Jessica swallowed hard, looking away.

Leandro seemed not to notice her reaction. 'You know,' he was saying musingly, 'I don't think I've ever met a woman who had as low an opinion of me as you have, Jessica. In its way, it is a salutary experience.' His eyes narrowed against the brilliant sky. After a thoughtful pause he went on. 'Almost like a challenge.'

'No!' said Jessica forcefully.

He turned his melting golden gaze on her, one eyebrow raised in enquiry.

'Absolutely no challenge,' she said with great firmness. 'Not a smidgin. I don't play out of my league.'

'You don't play at all,' pointed out Leandro gently. 'It is a great pity.'

'I'm not paid to play,' she reminded him. 'Paid very well, what's more.'

He gave a crooked smile. 'My uncle always buys the best and pays the going rate. I'm sure you could play a little more and still earn your fee.'

'Not if I spend long hours quarrelling with you,' Jessica said ruefully. 'I've got to go, Leandro.' She wished she did not sound so apologetic—or so regretful. 'I've got a feasibility study and outline plans to produce by the end of the month.'

He shrugged, indifferent. 'Then go and produce them, *cara*. I may deplore it, but I cannot stop you.'

'You *have* stopped me,' she pointed out, going. 'For a good half-hour.'

'That,' said Leandro drily, 'is progress.'

Though it cost Jessica dear, she let him have the last word. It was preferable to prolonging the encounter. For one thing, she was working to a very tight deadline and really did have too much work for comfort. For another, although she teased him about his film-star looks and sybarite existence, she was becoming aware that she was not as immune to Leandro Volpi's famed charm as she might have expected. This was as unwelcome as it was unforeseen; his company was therefore best avoided.

Jessica was cool-headed and ambitious. She had, moreover, only too good a reason to know what havoc emotional entanglements could cause in the lives of the unwary. There was no place in her life for a romantic interlude with anybody, least of all the playboy nephew of one of her most valued clients. She reminded herself of that fact sternly as she made her way to her state room.

The files awaiting her were stacked neatly on her desk. She observed the fact ruefully. Jessica, particularly when in one of her creative phases, worked in furious bursts, strewing papers, books, files, plans and plastic folders about every conceivable surface. When she had left for Genoa airport to collect Sue, the desk, and a goodly proportion of the Persian carpet, had been covered in exactly this manner. In her absence, obviously, the attentive cabin staff had restored order to chaos.

Jessica sighed. Neat as her cabin now was, it would take her ages to restore it to the inspirational disorder in which she needed to work. She was surveying it dispiritedly when a scratch came at the door.

'Come in,' she called.

It was Sue.

'I've rested as much as I can bear,' she announced, 'and I'm dying of curiosity. Are you available for conversation?'

'It looks like it, doesn't it?' said Jessica, with a gesture at the orderly desk.

Sue's eyes followed the indignantly pointed finger and widened.

'But you said you'd already started work this morning—oh!' Sue broke off. She looked at Jessica in mingled sympathy and amusement. 'You've been tidied up after,' she deduced.

Jessica nodded gloomily. Sue, to her great credit, maintained a straight face. She knew how Jessica felt about having her papers organised. Indeed, Sue had only got the job with the rising architectural practice of Shelburne and Lamont five years ago because she had understood Jessica's feelings so readily.

Sue had been, as she knew herself, much too young and inexperienced to be secretary to the senior partner of a dynamic company with an increasing international practice. Jessica had been working on a major oil complex development for a Near-Eastern government at the time. It had been heady stuff for an eighteen-year-old just out of secretarial college, particularly when she realised that her predecessors had all been efficient forty-year-olds with super grooming and innumerable language qualifications.

But Jessica had been adamant. 'You can pick up the languages—you only need a few phrases in each—and we'll pay you enough to buy designer clothes if that's what you think is necessary. What *I* need in a secretary is good sense, good humour, the ability to work long hours if necessary. And above all the ability to keep her hands off my papers while I'm working.' She had glared at Sue across her enormous, over-burdened desk. 'Can you handle *that?*'

Much amused, after her initial nervousness, Sue had said she thought so.

She had handled it so spectacularly that she now had a secretary of her own. She frequently accompanied Jessica when she travelled on business, as she often did. Giorgio di Stefano's yacht was, however, a new experience for Sue, though she knew that Jessica had been aboard a couple of times for discussions before she had agreed to accept Prince Giorgio's commission.

Now, looking at the devastatingly tidy desk, Sue asked with only the faintest quiver in her voice, 'Did you know the staff were this—er—conscientious?'

Jessica shook her head. 'They haven't been before. I told the chief steward not to touch things while I was working and he agreed. I suppose it must be different this time because I'm here for a month instead of just a weekend.' She looked despondent.

Sue chuckled. 'I'll speak to the steward and see if we can work out an honourable compromise,' she said soothingly. 'If I hold the plans down, some maid can whisk a feather duster over them and then we'll all be happy.'

Jessica's frown disappeared as if by magic. 'Thank God for you, Sue,' she said fervently.

'Right,' said Sue, 'I'll handle that. And—as you obviously can't plunge straight back into work until you've rebuilt your nest—what about a drink? You can give me a guided tour of the dos and don'ts of life aboard a luxury yacht. And a potted biography of the resident wildlife.'

Jessica laughed. 'Oh, very well.' She flung herself back on a deceptively fragile Louis Quinze chair—on which plan and elevation drawings of a four-bedroomed villa had been displayed earlier—and pressed a bell push in the wall. 'There are drinks of some sort in every cabin—cognac, gin and tonic, that sort of thing. But when there are guests on board, the Prince has the crew provide permanent room service. So you can order whatever you want at the press of a button. It's jolly useful if you get lost, too. You have no idea how big this damned boat is until you're late for a meeting.'

The telephone on Jessica's desk rang. She picked it up, listened and then said, 'Thank you, yes. I didn't lean on it by mistake this time.' There was laughter from the other end of the line. 'Miss York is with me and we were wondering about drinks in my cabin.' She paused. 'Yes, that would be fine, thank you. Oh, the usual for me, and for Miss York. . .' she flicked an eyebrow up at Sue who mouthed 'white wine' at her, '. . . white wine.' She listened again and then said in amusement, 'No, *not* champagne at this hour, Enrico. Her shorthand goes haywire on champagne. Some nice cold local vintage with minimal alcohol content would be best.'

She put the telephone down. Sue glared at her, mock-outraged.

'Are you trying to spoil my fun, Jessica? I may never have the chance to drink champagne at four o'clock in the afternoon again,' she complained.

'Oh yes, you will,' Jessica assured her drily. 'On this boat you can get it at four in the morning if you want it. It's Leandro Volpi's favourite beverage, I'm told, so they're not going to run out.'

'Really?' Sue was intrigued.

'Yes, really.' Jessica sounded almost irritated. 'The man's a complete cliché.'

'I thought he seemed rather nice,' said Sue mildly. She surveyed Jessica carefully. 'Not as patronising as I'd expected,' she added, 'or as vain.'

Since this was very much an echo of Jessica's own former thoughts there was really no excuse for her reaction to Sue's remark.

'Vain?' she echoed in patent disbelief. 'The man's a walking monument to vanity! Do you know he spends all day lying in the sun? When we first met, I asked him what he did for a living, what he worked at, and do you know what he said? His tan!' Her voice was full of scorn.

Sue gave a choke of laughter. 'Well, he seems to have done it very successfully,' she murmured.

Jessica snorted. 'So would anyone who did nothing but concentrate on his physical appearance.'

'But you must admit he has excellent material to work on,' observed Sue, still chuckling. 'Don't you always say that the secret of success is to capitalise on your natural assets?'

'And Leandro Volpi does that, I agree,' Jessica acknowledged drily. 'With dedication.'

There was a short knock at the door, which opened to reveal a smiling man in white, sporting epaulettes and gold buttons on his jacket along with a small shield-shaped embroidered motif on his breast pocket.

'Thank you, Enrico,' said Jessica, standing up to take from him the silver tray he was carrying.

'It is nothing, *signorina*.' He smiled. 'Can I get you anything else? Tea, perhaps? Later? You will be joining Signor Leandro for cocktails in the stern saloon at eight?'

Although it was phrased as a question, it sounded more like a piece of advice, Sue thought. She looked at the steward curiously. Had Jessica given offence by turning down the family invitations? Or by failing to turn up to meals? Sue knew that when Jessica was working she would ignore all distractions, including the necessity to be gracious to clients, and was quite likely to lose all sense of time.

Her suspicions were confirmed when Jessica made a face.

'You mean, will I turn up of my own free will, or have Signor Leandro come to fetch me?' she interpreted ruefully. 'All right, Enrico, I won't forget. Miss York,' she added with a gleam of fun, 'is here to remind me of things like that. It's part of her job. You can stand down now.'

He smiled back but said gently, 'The *signor* was most anxious that you should attend, *signorina*.'

He closed the door behind him on Jessica's sigh.

'Trouble?' asked Sue, scenting it.

Jessica was pouring a faintly greenish wine into a long-stemmed Venetian glass.

'Here you are,' she said, not answering. 'They tell me Ligurian wine doesn't travel—and I certainly never remember having it before—but ice-cold like this, it's nectar.'

'Trouble, Jessica?' persisted Sue, accepting the wine but refusing to be deflected. 'With the gorgeous nephew and heir, maybe?'

Jessica looked slightly guilty. 'I have locked horns with the Body Beautiful once or twice,' she admitted.

Sue sighed. 'To the extent that he came and dragged you away from your desk kicking and screaming?' she asked wearily. 'Marched you bodily into a cocktail party to meet his associates?'

Jessica looked startled. 'Something like that,' she agreed. 'You're much too quick. How did you guess?'

'It wasn't too difficult. I've had to do much the same thing myself once or twice,' Sue observed in a dry tone.

'Oh.' Jessica began to look amused. 'Yes, I suppose you have.' She wrinkled her nose. 'But at least in your case the party was full of people with whom I had business. The Body Beautiful just dumped me in the middle of a stampede of Riviera play people. I didn't see the point of it.'

Sue sighed again. She liked Jessica. She admired her work, enjoyed her company, and trusted her as she trusted few friends. She had no opinion, however, of her tact and diplomacy.

'I suppose you said so?' she asked in a resigned tone.

'Well, I did get rather cross.' Jessica flashed her an amused glance. 'Don't look like that, Sue. I wasn't rude—on my honour, I wasn't.' She paused, considering. 'Well, maybe I was a little rude. But only to the Body Beautiful, who doesn't count.'

Sue looked appalled. She took a long draught of her wine and then said in a suffocated voice, 'The adored only nephew of our most important client doesn't count?'

Jessica shrugged. 'He takes no interest in Prince Giorgio's business. He just lounges around, topping up his suntan and flexing his biceps at passing females.' This was unfair and she knew it. 'I doubt if he even knows which project I'm working on for Prince Giorgio. And cares less.' This was not.

'He might care about having you thrown off the project, though,' Sue said crisply and, as Jessica looked bewildered, explained with patience, 'I mean, if you antagonise him. People are odd like that—touchy, even vengeful, if you get them on a sore spot. If you've been attacking his ego—and frankly, Jessica, that sounds exactly what you've been up to—he may want to get his own back on you quite badly.'

Jessica looked shocked. 'Oh, I don't think so. He's not spiteful or anything like that. He wouldn't be petty.'

'You know him so well?' asked Sue politely.

'Me? No, of course not. He's not my sort of person.' Jessica looked flustered for a moment. 'But I'm still

positive he wouldn't do anything mean. Not like that.'
She hesitated. 'He's not the type.' And then, as Sue still
looked disbelieving, she added, 'He couldn't be bothered. I'm not that important to him.'

In some agitation she seized the other glass from the
tray and gulped some of the dark liquid it contained. Sue
watched her thoughtfully. She decided to change the
subject.

'Have you taken to drinking Coke to keep a clear
head?' she asked, indicating the drink.

'No, of course not.' Jessica was affronted. 'This is
Enrico's special iced coffee. He makes it for me when I
want to work late and leaves it in a Thermos on my desk.'

Sue was impressed. 'Every consideration! Is Prince
Giorgio so anxious for the plans?'

Jessica considered, frowning. 'No, I don't think so. It's
just his standard of courtesy, I think. Guests on the boat
have whatever they want: champagne, midnight coffee,
whatever.' She chuckled. 'They're even allowed to drive
the speedboat, I'm told, though it sends the mechanic in
charge of it into a frenzy!'

'Have you tried?' asked Sue, surprised. She knew that
Jessica had a phobia, which she never spoke about and
normally tried to suppress, about speed.

Jessica shuddered. 'Good God, no! Leandro challenged me to try, though, and I saw the look of horror
on the poor old mechanic's face.'

'How did you get out of it?'

Jessica shrugged. 'Told him I didn't have the time, and
that I didn't like being driven in a speedboat either. That,'
she added reflectively, 'was one of the things that
annoyed him about me, I think.'

Sue closed her eyes. 'No doubt,' she said carefully, 'he
would have liked the opportunity to demonstrate his
skill.'

'Put me in my place by showing off, you mean?' translated Jessica. 'Maybe you're right. Well, no harm done,' she added.

'I hope he thought so,' Sue said drily. 'Presumably time will tell. At least the standard of service hasn't gone down yet.' She wriggled pleasurably on the deep sofa. 'Are we really treated as guests?'

'Really, really.' Jessica nodded her head vigorously. 'It's a bit of a nuisance in some ways—they're always summoning you to come and meet some new visitor. But they mean to be kind.'

'And Prince Giorgio is here?'

'On board, you mean? No, most of the time not. He'll take her cruising at Christmas, but during the summer she's just moored here marking time.'

'So where is the Prince?'

Jessica shrugged. 'Rome, Florence, Paris; Milan sometimes. . . I don't keep track. His secretary can always find him. Now she *is* on board. I'm not quite sure why. Enrico said something about her recuperating after an illness, but she looks bursting with rude health to me.'

She heard the equivocal note in Jessica's voice. 'You don't like her?'

Jessica hesitated. 'She's very efficient. And she always does what I ask.'

'But?'

'But—I'm not sure.' She was thoughtful. 'She's very correct. And beautiful, too, I suppose, in a gymnastic sort of way. She's just not very friendly—I suppose that's what I mean. And all the others—the crew, the occasional guest, even the Body Beautiful—are so relaxed and friendly! Maybe the poor woman just suffers by comparison. Anyway, see what you think when you meet her.'

'I will,' promised Sue, intrigued. 'And is that it? The crew, the secretary, the Body Beautiful and us?'

'For the moment.'

'That doesn't sound too bad,' Sue remarked, holding out her glass for Jessica to replenish it. 'At least you won't be trying to work with a full-scale yacht party going on around you.'

'Except if Leandro has one of his weekends,' Jessica said gloomily. 'I gather they're legendary.' She sipped her coffee. 'Enrico says there's nothing planned at the moment, but Leandro might change his mind. He's the type to give a major party at a moment's notice on a whim,' she said bitterly. 'If only to annoy me.'

Sue laughed, shaking her head. 'Your paranoia is showing! I'm sure he wouldn't. The crew wouldn't stand for it.'

'The crew,' said Jessica with bite, 'think he's wonderful. If he told each and every one of them to walk the plank, they'd probably do it.'

'They wouldn't like to have a big party sprung on them, though,' said Sue with feeling. She had experienced just such an eventuality several times since she had joined Shelburne and Lamont.

'They would love it,' Jessica contradicted her flatly. 'They'd think it was the most terrific game. It's part of why they're so crazy about Leandro: they never know what he's going to do next. They keep telling me,' she sounded despairing, 'how spontaneous he is. *Spontaneous!* What they mean is, he's hare-brained and completely unpredictable.'

Intrigued by this surprising outburst, Sue chose her words carefully. 'He certainly seems to have stirred you up.'

'Well, it's very unsettling,' said Jessica defensively. 'And he's quite capable of having an orgy here on the spur of the moment. That's one of the reasons I'm working flat out.'

'To make your escape before the orgy?' murmured Sue, teasing.

'Exactly. Leandro would think it very funny,' Jessica said obscurely.

'How far have you got?' asked Sue, when it was obvious Jessica was not going to confide further.

'First phase complete,' was the complacent answer. 'That's why you're here. I need it typed up and bound and circulated to Prince Giorgio and his people, to say nothing of the officials. I don't know what planning consent difficulties we may have; Prince Giorgio is too casual about it for my liking. I don't think it's going to be as simple as he wants to believe, but his local experts bear him out so far, so maybe I'm making a fuss about nothing. Anyway, after that we're into layout and unit design. I've got some sketches.'

Sue nodded. To her experienced ears it sounded as if the project was moving fast.

'Snags?' she asked.

Jessica was thoughtful. 'None at all so far. It's been almost too easy. Something in my bones tells me it won't last.'

'You foresee difficulties?' Sue frowned. 'Where exactly?'

It was a big project, but most of the partnership's fee depended on it being successfully built. If it was not completed, though they would of course be paid for Sue's and Jessica's time, there would be no percentage fee, Sue knew.

'Not foresee,' said Jessica tranquilly. She tapped her nose. 'Smell. Call it a hunch. Don't look so appalled, Sue. Sorting out difficulties is my forte.' She grinned. 'It makes my otherwise boring life exciting!'

CHAPTER TWO

WHEN Sue left, Jessica looked at her tidy desk with a sigh. She had never, she acknowledged to herself, felt less like working in her life. Nor was it entirely due to the unwelcome ordering of her papers; she had been aware of a restlessness for days. All the time she had been working, she had been aware of a profound dissatisfaction, as if she were looking over her shoulder waiting for something more important to invite her attention.

Jessica sighed again. There was no reason for it. Despite her hunch—and her unusual difficulty with concentration—the project was coming along well and ahead of schedule. Prince Giorgio, whose original idea the project had been, was enthusiastic. She was living in delightful surroundings, her every wish complied with. On a broader canvas, she had no financial or personal worries. Her mouth twisted wryly; it would be more accurate to say that she had dealt with her financial and personal worries and was not going to let such things recur. And she was rapidly scaling the peak of her profession. So what was wrong?

Jessica sat back in the delicate chair, shifting her shoulders restlessly against the tapestry back. A frown crossed her brow, drawing the decided eyebrows together in a black line across her face. She caught sight of the fierce expression in a mirror on the other side of the cabin and was startled by it. Good heavens, she looked like a harridan!

She stood up and went to the mirror. It was oval in a heavily embossed gilt frame; probably eighteenth-century, she thought ruefully, like so many of the yacht's furnishings. The face that stared back at her, though, was far removed from the delicate prettiness of eighteenth-century beauties.

The brows were too marked, Jessica decided dispassionately. The chin was certainly too decisive. Her widely spaced green eyes, inherited from a mother more famed for her looks than her common sense, were striking, of course. It was a memorable face, she supposed, with its spare bone structure, inherited from a dozen dissolute but aristocratic Shelburnes. And she had her gentle mother's fall of chestnut hair, too, although Jessica usually kept it knotted tidily at the nape of her neck. Loose it made her look—and feel—altogether too youthful.

She leaned forward, inspecting herself. Yes, every feature had had its forerunner in the family portraits which had been sold, every one, to Uncle Richard. Her mouth tightened at the thought. That mouth, though she would never have been brought to admit it, was the single clue in an otherwise impeccable front that she might not be as cool-headed and passionless as she liked to appear. Or as invulnerable.

Jessica had made it a point of principle never to be vulnerable to anyone or anything. She had made sure that she never put herself in anyone's power. She conducted her personal life with the sole objective of never, under any circumstances, leaving herself open to hurt.

Of course, there were reasons for that. Unconsciously she sighed. The reflected image took on a wistful expression which Jessica, turning away from it, did not notice. It made her look younger, in spite of the severe hairstyle, and uncharacteristically fragile.

There were times when she even regretted her toughness, she acknowledged to herself. Sometimes she wondered whether she could have been different. If her father had not died when he did, leaving her mother in

such straits with eight-year-old Jessica to bring up, would
she have been different? If she had not learned, almost
before she knew what money was, that men would cheat
and betray to get it, would she have been different then?
If she had not watched her mother through the painful
cycle of trust, doubt, disbelief and in the end desperate
hurt, would she, Jessica, have been a nicer person? It was
the hurt that had been so bad, she realised, for both of
them. Beside the betrayal of confidence, the financial loss
was almost irrelevant. It was not poverty that had wiped
the laughter out of her mother's eyes for ever, though at
times they had been nearly destitute. It was Richard
Dempster's betrayal.

She moved her shoulders uncomfortably, pushing the
memory away from her. Her mother was all right now,
installed in a pretty house in a village where she had
found friends. Her financial worries had been wiped out
by Jessica's success; she was now secure. The trouble,
thought Jessica, was that there was nothing she could do
to take away the residual sadness. Her mother had loved
and trusted Richard Dempster, and nothing could make
up to her for the disaster he had wrought.

She shrugged, suddenly impatient with herself. None
of these thoughts was new, nor could she do anything
about them. Why was she brooding in her cabin, picking
over her character and wondering whether her treasured
independence was quite worth what it had cost? She was
not restless and introspective at home; why here?

She started to frown again blackly. She knew the
answer to the question and was too honest not to admit
it. She did not like doing so, however. It was utterly
unreasonable that a butterfly like Leandro Volpi should
have the ability to stir her up like this with his teasing.
It was not even as if it mattered to him.

Not, she reminded herself sternly, that it mattered to
her, either. She did not care a snap of her fingers what

Leandro Volpi thought of her. His comments were only upsetting because they made her look harder at herself and she did not altogether like what she saw. Leandro Volpi was just an incidental irritant.

She began to work. It was in a desultory fashion, though, unusual for Jessica. The incidental irritant kept intruding on her concentration until she could have screamed with annoyance. Within an hour she was pushing her writing pad away from her and looking at her watch.

It was still too early for cocktails, even on this hospitable boat. The foredeck would therefore still be free from revellers. If she slipped into her bikini and went to sunbathe now, she ought to be able to manage an hour or so basking on her own. The evening rays were too weak to attract Leandro, who stretched out in the full heat of midday. And the stewards would not start to set out tables and canapé dishes in expectation of the inevitable guests until the sun finally began to sink into the sea.

She found that she had, to some extent, miscalculated. It was certainly too early for the staff to be preparing. The foredeck, however, was not uninhabited as she had hoped and expected.

'Hello, *carissima*,' said Leandro from his sun-lounger, not opening his eyes. 'Decided to join me at last?'

Jessica hesitated at the top of the companionway. She was suddenly horribly conscious of her bare feet and the fragility of the cotton shirt she had thrown over her bikini. Summoning her courage, she walked forward. She was being foolish, she told herself; Leandro could not have looked less threatening.

'Good afternoon,' she said composedly. 'I was hoping to get in a little evening sunbathing. If that wouldn't disturb you?'

The beautiful mouth quirked.

'*Cara* Jessica, you disturb me all the time,' he murmured, barely moving his lips.

He did not turn his head to look at her, or otherwise move from his utterly relaxed posture. His very indolence, she thought, gave the lie to the provocative remark. As usual, his objective was presumably solely to make her uncomfortable. Well, he would not succeed.

She surveyed the still, beautiful body with dislike before seating herself on another lounger, as far as possible from him.

'I'm sorry about that,' she said crisply.

She flexed her toes against the deck. It was warm underfoot from a whole day's sun. With a little sigh of contentment she swung her legs on to the lounger and gazed up at the hazy sky.

'You have some sun cream?' asked Leandro idly.

Jessica frowned; then, remembering how she had looked in the mirror, she hastily changed her expression.

'Why?' Damn the man! She sounded like a hysterical spinster, instantly suspicious, much too guarded.

Leandro clearly shared her own thoughts. 'Why, so I can get my hands on you, *bellissima,* by covering you with sticky goo,' he said drily. He gave a little chuckle. 'Insect repellent would do,' he offered as an apparent afterthought.

Jessica blushed, yet she was reassured by this mockery, even while she was embarrassed by it.

'Yes, I suppose I did think that was what you meant,' she admitted. 'I'm sorry.'

Leandro gave a faint shrug, a minimal movement of the tanned shoulders.

'Don't apologise, *cara.* My reputation would be on the wane if that had not been what you thought.' Suddenly he turned his head and opened his eyes, looking full at her with that direct gaze. It struck her oddly that, when he was not mocking or assuming that melting look, his eyes were very sharp.

'But on this occasion, I was motivated entirely by concern. You are very pale and even in September this sun can be fierce. You will have an uncomfortable time if you ignore sensible precautions against it.'

'Even at this hour?' Jessica was startled.

'By my standards, my English rose, this is cool,' Leandro said drily, resuming his former position and addressing the sky from behind closed lids. 'In fact I am being immensely macho in staying out here without putting on a tracksuit to protect me from the breeze.'

'Well then. . .'

'I said by my standards. Your standards are different. As,' he added mischievously, 'you never cease to tell me. After a summer of English rain—which you probably spent cooped up in an office, anyway—I imagine this is high grilling temperature to your skin. You should use a sun blocker, at least to begin with. If you haven't brought any, ask Enrico. I know Giorgio keeps things like that for his guests.'

'I will,' promised Jessica, letting her eyes drift closed under the soothing rays.

'Now,' Leandro said gently.

For a moment Jessica was tempted to mutiny. Then she gave a small shrug and sat up. It was for her own good, after all. Little as she relished Leandro's tone of cool command, she had to admit that his advice was sensible.

Sighing, she swung her feet to the ground again.

'Where are you going?'

'As instructed,' Jessica said drily.

'I didn't tell you to run away.' Leandro gave her an ardent, melting look that made her want to hit him. 'It is hard enough for me to get a few minutes in your company; would I send you away?'

'You told me to fetch some sun cream.'

'Wrong.' He shook his head, gently rebuking her. 'I told you to use sun cream. Enrico will fetch it—that's what he's paid for.'

He reached out a long-fingered hand and touched a bell in the wall behind him.

Jessica snorted, torn between anger and amusement.

'There's no reason why I shouldn't fetch my own. I'm not an honoured guest, I'm an employee. Enrico isn't here to wait on *me*.'

'And you think he shouldn't wait on me, either.' Leandro did not try to disguise his amusement. 'You think I'm an idle fellow, don't you, *cara?*'

Jessica looked away, faintly uncomfortable.

'Don't you?' he persisted.

Seeing that he was not to be deflected, she answered carefully, 'I think you are rather more—shall we say laid back?—than I am.'

He grunted. 'My dear child, a hang-glider in a snow-storm would be more laid back than you are. I've never seen a woman twitch so much. You're never still!'

Stung, Jessica snapped, 'Just because you never move if you can help it!' and found herself, quite unexpectedly, looking up into laughing eyes that were altogether too near. Leandro shook his head, the sun glinting on the golden lights in his disarranged hair. He must have been swimming, she thought confusedly; the springy brown hair was not quite dry at the ends and he smelt of salt.

'How wrong you are,' said Leandro, laughing at her.

And his mouth closed, softly and warmly, over her own.

Jessica did not struggle. For one thing she was too surprised. For another, although the embrace was of exemplary lightness and gentleness, she had a sudden and inexplicable tremor of trepidation, sensing that the beautiful body owned a leashed strength which she would not previously have suspected. So she stayed still as a startled mouse under his kiss.

Eventually he raised his head. He was smiling.

'There you are,' he said.

She looked at him warily. '*Where* am I?'

Leandro laughed. 'In the wrong. Admit it.'

'*I'm* in the wrong because you kiss me?' Jessica queried drily.

'You accused me of never moving unless I could help it,' he reminded her, his eyes glinting. 'I demand a retraction.'

She allowed a note of mockery to enter her voice. 'Kissing is moving?'

He chuckled. 'Well, it moves me. You're obviously less susceptible.'

Jessica gave him a sweet false smile. She was fairly certain that he had made an accurate assessment of exactly how susceptible she was. The thought infuriated her, but she was not going to let him see that.

'I retract,' she told him. 'I misjudged you.'

'You did indeed,' he agreed tranquilly. He was still much too close, his arms on either side of her barring her escape, his expression wicked. 'Are you going to apologise?'

'Abjectly,' Jessica assured him.

He laughed, withdrawing. 'How very disappointing!'

She did not answer that one. She watched from under her lashes as he disposed his long limbs on the sun-lounger next to her own, and tilted his head back towards the sun. He must, she thought dispassionately, be the most handsome man she had ever met, and the most spoilt, the most irreverent, the most annoying. . .

Enrico's arrival interrupted her thoughts.

'You rang, *signor?*'

'Yes, indeed. Have we any sun cream for the *signorina*, Enrico?'

Jessica became aware that two pairs of eyes were considering her pale skin professionally. A faint flush rose in her cheeks as they discussed her requirements.

'The *signorina* is very fair,' Enrico was saying doubtfully. 'I do not think that any of the usual preparations that we keep would be advisable.'

'What about the American girl? Didn't she leave anything behind? She was a blonde.'

'Ah, but she did not have that delicate skin,' Enrico reminded him. 'It is the skin that goes with Titian hair, not with blonde.'

'You're right, of course,' Leandro agreed. 'Well, Gina's a redhead. What about her stuff?'

'The Contessa has her cosmetics made up individually,' Enrico said, clearly doubtful. 'The *signorina* might be allergic. . .'

'Oh God, yes, they smell, don't they?' Leandro agreed cheerfully.

'They are highly perfumed,' agreed Enrico in a neutral voice, though Jessica had the strong impression that he was laughing.

She sat up. 'Look,' she said, 'no doubt you mean to be kind, but. . .'

Enrico and Leandro stopped their conversation and looked at her with kindly and mildly surprised enquiry. As if, she thought dourly, some pampered poodle had suddenly voiced a preference for back-combing.

'It's not that hot,' she said firmly. 'I'll buy my own cream tomorrow. And for tonight, if you really think it inadvisable for me to stay out here,' she said to Leandro deferentially, 'I'll go back to my cabin.'

'That would be a shame,' he said smoothly. 'I am sure Enrico will be able to find you something that will do for now. And I will take you into Portofino myself tomorrow to buy something more satisfactory.'

'Thank you,' said Jessica woodenly.

Enrico left them, trying, and failing, to hide his grin. Oh, hell, another boost to shipboard gossip, thought Jessica. She flung herself back on the lounger and tried to calm her temper. Her hands were curled into tight fists. Slowly she relaxed them, stretching out each finger, one at a time, and breathing deeply. She sensed that Leandro was watching this manoeuvre with some amusement. She ignored him.

At length he said, 'Did you really not bring any lotions with you? You can't have used them all up. I haven't seen you sunbathing before.'

'I'm here to work,' she reminded him, refraining from admitting that on every occasion when she had thought of sunbathing she had been driven from the deck by his presence.

'But not all the time,' he protested. 'Surely even in London you enjoy yourself sometimes.'

'I enjoy my work,' Jessica said coldly. She regretted it immediately; she sounded priggish.

'And that is all you enjoy?'

'What do you mean?'

'Well, we have established that you don't expect to sunbathe—though the weather and this countryside, to say nothing of the yacht, were created for it. And you don't like talking to my friends. You don't want to drive the speedboat. So,' he turned his head, his eyes gleaming, 'how do you get your kicks, Jessica Shelburne?'

There was a faint prickly tremor running along her spine. She was, she realised in some annoyance, just the slightest bit afraid of Leandro Volpi and his teasing. Oh, she was not afraid that he might lay violent hands on her, or anything like that, but he was too cool, too sophisticated; she was not sure she could match him. And she was very afraid that, if she did not match him, she might at best look a fool, at worst get badly hurt.

She therefore said with great calmness, 'I drink.'

'*What?*' He jack-knifed up in one fluid movement, staring at her.

That bounced him out of his complacent mockery! Jessica thought with satisfaction.

'Rather a lot, actually,' she said in a deadpan voice.

He regarded her narrowly for a moment or two. Then he smiled. 'Mineral water?' he asked, plainly undeceived.

Her annoyance increased, but she did not allow it to appear. 'Iced coffee, actually.'

His voice was filled with unholy amusement. 'Well, it figures.'

'It does?'

'It must help keep the blood in your veins at sub-zero temperature,' he explained innocently. 'A primary requirement of ice maidens, I suppose.'

Jessica said between her teeth, '*I am not an ice maiden.*'

'No?' He crossed his legs and sat in the lotus position, regarding her prone body with his head on one side. 'Have you any empirical evidence?'

She opened one eye and glared at him. 'Just because I haven't thrown myself at your head. . .'

'*Carissima,* it is I who have thrown myself at you,' he confessed charmingly, 'and have the frostbite to prove it.'

She opened both eyes, turned her head and allowed herself a long admiring survey of his tanned frame.

'Believe me, it doesn't show,' she told him.

He gave a shout of laughter then. 'How would you know? I bet you've never seen a man who hasn't got frostbite.'

Jessica said coldly, 'You're very insulting.'

'Yes, I suppose I am,' he agreed without noticeable remorse.

'If I'd known that I would be subjected to these sort of personal remarks,' she said, with what she could not disguise from herself was horrible pomposity, 'I should have refused to stay on this boat. You have no right to talk to me in this way. And I don't see why you should want to—unless it's some nasty way of amusing yourself.'

'It's a very effective way,' Leandro said unrepentantly.

She glared at him. He smiled back sunnily. She considered, and rejected, the possibility of hitting him. Enrico would no doubt return at the critical moment and then the gossip would really take fire. Besides, she was by no means sure that Leandro would take a smacked face like an officer and a gentleman. She had the distinct impression that he would retaliate, swiftly and with interest.

After a pause he continued, 'You know, for such a very untouchable lady, you have an extraordinarily thin skin.'

There were a number of answers to that and every one of them would take her into very deep water indeed. She thought that Leandro was well aware of it.

She ignored him deliberately and sank back in the lounger, closing her eyes.

'Don't you have to get ready for your party?' she asked in a neutral voice.

'It is not a party. Merely a few friends coming for drinks and even fewer staying for dinner.'

She grimaced. 'So what is a party, in your terms?'

Leandro gave a soft laugh. 'Oh, at least a hundred people and two bands,' he told her with complete sangfroid.

Jessica sniffed. 'I believe you.'

'I thought you would.' He shifted and her eyes flew open suspiciously, but he was just making himself more comfortable on his own lounger. Jessica found he was looking across at her in undisguised amusement. 'You really don't think at all highly of me, do you?'

'I have no opinion on the subject,' she said loftily.

He ignored that. 'I've never met anyone who disapproved of me as comprehensively as you do,' he said in a meditative tone. 'I sometimes wonder why. Are you measuring me by some paragon of manly virtue at home?'

Jessica was not sure that he required an answer; he sounded almost as if he was talking to himself. So she preserved a prudent silence.

'What sort of man would you approve of, now?' Leandro went on thoughtfully.

He was clearly determined to annoy her. Jessica set her teeth. She would not rise to his teasing, she promised herself.

'A worker, of course. A hard worker. Perhaps even a workaholic?' He cocked an enquiring eyebrow at her. 'One of these dynamos that live on aeroplanes and touch down for some private life three times a year. Yes, I can imagine that suiting you very well.'

Before she could stop herself she snapped, 'I can't imagine that would suit any woman!'

Too late she realised she had fallen into his trap. He gave her his most brilliant smile. 'Quite.'

She said wryly, 'Are you trying to tell me I'm unfeminine?'

Leandro grinned. 'You are all too feminine, *cara*. Much too feminine for my peace of mind. But so very unsusceptible.' And he shook his head mournfully.

About to deny the accusation hotly, Jessica paused. Maybe it was true. And even if it was not, it was no bad thing that Leandro Volpi thought she was unsusceptible.

He said curiously, 'Have you ever been in love, Jessica?'

She gave him a startled look. In spite of the teasing, the question sounded almost serious.

'Why?' she demanded suspiciously.

He shrugged. 'Because I find you a puzzle. I cannot account for it.'

'Account for what? That I didn't fall flat at your feet?' she asked ironically.

He chuckled. 'That was, of course, unique.' Then, growing serious again, 'But no. I mean rather this feeling you seem to have that it is wrong to enjoy yourself. And that people who enjoy themselves are some sort of delinquents.'

She moved sharply, raising her hand in silent protest.

'Well, no, maybe that is unjust. Let us say lightweight. That is better. You think people who enjoy themselves are by definition profoundly unserious people. Not your sort of people. You despise them.'

Jessica said, 'I don't think that's quite fair.'

But the quiet voice went on inexorably. 'You divide the world into two: those who work all the time, and those who play a little sometimes. And the latter are butterflies not worth your consideration.' Was there a touch of bitterness in the smooth voice now?

'I don't think my judgments are quite as sweeping as that,' said Jessica, shaken.

'I assure you they are.' He shifted on to his side and, propping himself on one elbow, turned to look at her. 'Take myself, for example.'

Jessica was suspicious. 'Why?'

'A butterfly, right? A drone, not a worker. An unserious person. You took one look at me and made your assessment.'

She said incredulously, 'Are you trying to tell me you're one of the workers of the world?'

A wry smile curled the beautiful mouth. 'There you are! That is exactly my point. Because I play a little. . .'

'A *little?*' echoed Jessica, strongly moved. 'All day in the sun? That damned great car? Champagne on tap?'

The smile grew. 'And because of these trappings,' Leandro said softly, 'you have made up your mind about me once and for all. No hesitation, no second thoughts. Subject tried and condemned.' His eyes glinted. 'But what if I were to tell you I am a hard-working engineer?'

'I wouldn't believe you,' Jessica said calmly. 'No hard-working engineer ever had that sort of tan.'

There was a short silence.

'No, of course not. How perceptive of you.' He sank back again, his hands behind his head, and surveyed the cloudless sky. 'I am encouraged that you noticed, though,' he added wickedly.

Jessica felt herself blush and cast him a look of dislike.

'It's not easy to miss, especially when you're on the boat all the time.'

He asked softly, 'Do I disturb you, Jessica?'

She hesitated. 'It's your boat.'

'My uncle's,' Leandro corrected. 'And that was not what I asked.'

Well, of course, she wasn't going to answer that. She allowed the silence to lengthen, hoping that he was drifting off to sleep in the late sun. She herself felt oddly tense, in spite of the warmth and the peace. She had very little trouble in ascribing her tension to Leandro's presence, which, of course, answered his question, although she was not going to give him the satisfaction of telling him so.

Maybe it was because there were so few men in her life; so few people, if she were honest. Apart from her mother, now comfortably settled in her rural retreat, the only people Jessica saw regularly were colleagues.

She caught herself; perhaps a few business acquaintances, other architects, commissioning managers of major building firms, all of them people she saw from a sense of commercial obligation and put out of her mind the moment she left their company. Other than that, hers was a lonely life, she realised. It was what she sought, living alone, holidaying alone, keeping her occasional escorts at arm's length so that in the end they all moved on to more accommodating ladies.

Never once had Jessica been tempted to be more accommodating herself. When she closed the door of her flat on a persuasive suitor she would relax in relief and tuck herself up with work or a book. She knew that she was safe when she was on her own. With people you ran the risk of getting hurt.

She had tried to convey some of this to Leandro, but he took no notice. From her first visit to the yacht he had been deliberately provocative, ignoring alike her protests and her resistance. For once she felt out of control, as if she were a leaf being driven along by a strong wind. She did not like the sensation and said so, but Leandro only laughed and kissed her fingers.

Jessica had no idea why she did not simply avoid him altogether. He could scarcely order her to dine with him, after all. She cast a covert look at his profile, etched in unexpectedly stern beauty against the sky. Why did she have this feeling that if she did announce she did not intend to eat with him any more he would just ignore it and, if necessary, carry her down to the dining saloon every night?

She was used to dictating terms in her relationships. She was used to keeping herself aloof and untouched. Why then was it so impossible with Leandro? Was it sheer persistence on his part? He absolutely refused to notice her resistance and was striding rapidly towards the position where the crew would have every justification for their suspicions that he and the English architect lady were lovers. Or was it some failing in herself? He was too practised at charming much more sophisticated ladies than herself. And moreover, under his mock-wooing, Jessica had found that she was more than a little attracted to him. Though she did not, of course, approve of his principles or his way of life.

She looked at him again, tanned and somnolent and handsome. No, certainly she did not approve of him or the unprecedented effect he had on her responses.

At last he said, 'Have you ever played? Ever enjoyed yourself at all?'

She shifted uncomfortably. 'I enjoy my work.'

'Ah, yes. Naturally. I was forgetting.'

'It's very absorbing,' Jessica said, wishing she did not sound so defensive.

'Absorbing so much that you have no energy left to fall in love?' he asked, amused.

'Not at all. I——'

'So you *have* been in love,' he said with satisfaction.

Jessica was annoyed. 'No, I——'

'Have not been in love.' Leandro laughed. 'Just as I thought. It is a shocking state of affairs. I shall do something about it.'

'Has it occurred to you,' said Jessica with great restraint, 'that, while you were putting words into my mouth, what I actually might have meant was that I am in love now? Not in the past. Now.'

'No,' Leandro said positively. 'Absolutely no. Impossible.'

'It is not impossible.' If Jessica had been standing up— and twenty years younger—she would have stamped her foot. 'As you pointed out, I am wedded to my work,' she said recklessly. 'I should remind you that I work in partnership with a man.'

'And you are telling me that you are in love with this— partner?' Leandro queried, incredulity warring with disdain. The tone in which he said 'partner' could equally well have been used to say 'gnat'.

Jessica gave him a cool smile. 'I'm telling you nothing. But if you want to speculate about my private life, you should take Andrew into account.'

It was a total fabrication. She had never even thought of falling in love with Andrew, as would become very clear if Leandro were ever to meet him. She must make sure that they never did meet; at least, not until this assignment was over.

'My poor girl!' The eloquent voice was warm with sympathy. 'You are obviously in a very much worse situation than I thought.'

Jessica glared at him. 'Why is that?'

'Because you know so little of life that you do not even realise that you are not in love,' Leandro said softly. His eyes met hers. They were dancing with triumph, but there was something more there than the simple pleasure of having won their battle of words.

Jessica said, 'You're no judge of that.'

He said evenly, 'Oh, but I am.' And, as she stared at him, 'You cannot escape, you see, *cara* Jessica. If you judge me, I judge you. And God help both of us.'

CHAPTER THREE

JESSICA was late for dinner. She missed the cocktails entirely. She assured herself—and Sue when she came to fetch her—that it was not deliberate. But underneath she had the faint, lowering suspicion that that threatening remark of Leandro's, his last before Enrico returned with the sun cream, had left her wary and reluctant to return to his company.

It was not sensible, she told herself. He represented no danger to her. He was only a playboy; attractive, but a playboy nevertheless. She did not care what he thought of her, and, in spite of Sue's fear, she was sure that Prince Giorgio would not care either.

So why should it matter that he threw out that half laughing, half deadly serious challenge? All she had to do was ignore his overtures. She had done it before with other men without any great difficulty. Why should Leandro be different?

Yet he was, and it so annoyed Jessica that she flung herself into work so hard that she did not notice the sun's decline beyond her porthole, nor hear the dinner gong. She could not with equal justification say she did not notice the telephone when it purred into life across the cabin; she ignored it.

When Sue arrived she found Jessica sitting cross-legged on the floor, an enormous sheet of paper draped across her knees, drawing with great care, using a pen with a minute point, on the section she had braced against a clipboard.

'You'll tear the paper if you do it like that,' Sue observed.

49

She had knocked and, on not being answered, had entered anyway. She was accustomed to Jessica's habit of total concentration.

Jessica was frowning horribly over the paper. She looked up with a jump at Sue's words. Sue went down on her knees beside her and very carefully removed first the paper and then the clipboard.

'You know that the clip goes through the paper,' she said calmly.

Jessica looked mutinous. 'It doesn't matter. It's only a draft.'

'And you'll get furious with yourself if you mess it up and have to copy it all out again,' Sue pointed out reasonably. She knew Jessica's habit of impatience as well. 'I'll put it up on the drawing board for you tomorrow. Now come and eat.'

Jessica pushed a hand through her hair. As always when she was working, it had come loose from its confining scarf. Softly curling strands had wafted forward on to her cheek and lay feathered out along her neck. Sue surveyed them.

'If you don't come soon, Leandro will come and get you, I think,' she said dispassionately. 'Don't you want to—er—tidy up, first?'

For a moment Jessica looked almost panic-stricken. Sue was surprised and her brows rose. But at once the expression was gone and the other woman was calm again, if slightly harassed.

'Is it late?' she asked cautiously.

'The beautiful people have returned to their boats and their villas,' Sue agreed, amused. 'There's just you and me, a blonde who looks like a weight-lifter, and some sort of local government official who seems to be an old friend of the family.'

Jessica looked at her. Sue's lips twitched.

'And Leandro,' she added teasingly.

Jessica got to her feet with dignity. 'Naturally,' she said.

She went into the bedroom. Sue followed her and sat on a white-painted chair while Jessica riffled through her wardrobe and extracted a light, elegant jersey dress the colour of beech leaves in the autumn. Sue knew the dress. It was beautiful, but it was also very formal. Jessica wore it when she was in one of her crushing moods.

Sue looked at the dress speculatively while Jessica found underclothes and disappeared to shower. She was back inside five minutes and dressed in three. One thing you could say for Jessica, thought Sue, she might forget her appointments, but she could get ready faster than any other woman in the world. She told her so.

Jessica's worried expression lifted and she gave Sue a grin.

'Years of practice,' she admitted.

'Yes, I suppose so,' Sue said thoughtfully. 'But you usually only forget the parties you don't want to remember. Why don't you want to remember ordinary family dinner, Jess?'

Jessica shrugged, not answering.

'Has Leandro got to you, then?' pursued Sue, rather amused.

She was surprised at the furious look it earned her.

'Don't you start, too, for God's sake!' Jessica sighed. 'The whole crew are winding up for us to have a steaming affair.' The humour in her voice was forced, but for once Sue seemed not to notice.

'Then why don't you? Old Chinese proverbs and all that.'

Jessica smiled perfunctorily, but the green eyes darkened. She looked away, out at the blackness through the porthole. Sue watched curiously. The sudden gravity was unexpected and she wondered, with a little jolt, whether Jessica could possibly really have fallen for Leandro

Volpi. It seemed unlikely from what she knew of her, but unlikelier things had happened. And she certainly looked serious enough for it to be true.

'No,' Jessica said with a smile that was more sad than anything else. 'No, Sue. Not my style.' She gave herself a little shake and turned away from the porthole, picking up a wide brown leather belt and clipping it round her waist.

Sue was nonplussed. She had not expected her teasing to lead into realms of real feeling and was filled with compunction. She was, however, also curious; she ventured one last question.

'Might it not be fun to change your style, just for once?'

Jessica had her back to her. 'I changed it,' she said briefly, 'a long time ago.' And, as Sue stared at her, she turned round, saying with an effort at lightness, 'I know the Leandro Volpis of this world, Sue, better than you can imagine. And I don't get involved with them.'

They went to dinner almost in silence, Sue feeling faintly worried, though she could not have said exactly why. Jessica maintained an imperturbable front.

Her cool self-possession did not slip, even when they reached the deck and Leandro strolled towards them, taking Jessica's hand between both his own and caressing it openly.

'Late as always,' he said teasingly. 'Are you trying to make sure we appreciate your company properly?'

Jessica withdrew her hand. 'I doubt whether you have the slightest concept of what is proper,' she told him, but with a smile that took the sting out of the words. Or was intended to. Her eyes, Sue noted, stayed aloof. From his wry expression, she deduced that Leandro Volpi noticed it too.

He shook his head and smiled lazily down at her. 'You'll find you are wrong,' he murmured under his breath, as if he did not intend to be overheard.

Jessica fought a blush and pretended she did not hear him.

He sighed. 'Let me introduce you to my good friend Simone Spinoletti,' he said in quite a different tone. 'He is a very important man round here. Mayor of Castel San Giorgio, no less.'

Jessica's interest quickened.

'Really?' She held out her hand to the man, smiling. 'The village on the hill above the grotto?'

Spinoletti nodded, pleased. He looked quite young, probably younger than Leandro. He was short and very wiry. He looked as if he worked out of doors all day, from his tan and air of glowing health. Jessica liked him.

His outdoor air, however, was deceptive, she found over dinner.

'My family have worked the land for years,' he told her. 'Centuries. And I too have a little farm with corn and vines down the terraces. But I work in La Spezia.'

'Really?' She was surprised. She had thought the village too remote to be the home of commuters, and said so.

'Oh, I do not live in Castel San Giorgio during the week. I have an apartment in La Spezia.' He grimaced. 'But I am at home at weekends.'

'Is that not very complicated?' asked Jessica. 'Running a two-centre life like that?'

He nodded. 'And it does not make it any easier when I have to fight. . .' He broke off, looking confused, with a quick glance at Leandro that seemed to be begging for help.

Jessica was thoughtful. Fight? Fight Prince Giorgio's holiday development plans, maybe? She had thought that the Prince was altogether too casual about the attitude of the local authority. But what game was Leandro playing? She looked at him thoughtfully.

He had been talking to the woman he called Sandra, the statuesque blonde secretary. But now he turned, apparently sensing Jessica's eyes upon him.

He met her gaze enigmatically, his eyes very steady. He raised an eyebrow at her expression.

Beside her, Simone Spinoletti leaned forward.

'I have been talking too much, my friend,' he said ruefully.

Leandro's eyes did not leave Jessica's, though he answered his friend. 'Been spilling the beans, Sim?'

'Beans?' The man looked confused.

Leandro smiled into Jessica's eyes. 'Explain to the man, *carissima*.'

With an effort she dragged her eyes away from that mesmeric power.

'It means to—to tell everything, I suppose,' she said haltingly, trying to concentrate. 'Sort of—to confess.'

Simone Spinoletti made a face. 'As bad as that?'

Leandro gave a laugh, throwing his head back. 'Oh, poor Sim! One glance from the lovely enemy and you are a broken man!'

Enemy? Jessica's gaze swung back to him rapidly. Was she right, then? Was Spinoletti opposed to Prince Giorgio's plans?

She said carefully, 'I don't see what I've done to make me an enemy.'

Spinoletti was quite frank. 'It is not your fault,' he assured her generously. 'Prince Giorgio has certain—ideas—which are not very popular, that is all. You were not to know.'

'The village?'

Leandro said drily, 'Which village, Jessica? The one that exists? Or the pretty new one that my uncle wants to build and take all their water?'

Jessica let out a long breath. 'I see,' she murmured. 'Does he know of your objections?'

'Intimately,' said Leandro, smiling faintly.

Spinoletti looked uncomfortable. 'It is not a new project, you understand, *signorina*. For a while it was stopped. But now——' He shrugged.

'Now,' said Leandro very softly, 'he has employed Shelburne and Lamont of London to turn his ideas into reality.'

The blonde said sharply, 'This can hardly concern Miss Shelburne, Leo. She did not write her own brief.'

Leo, thought Jessica, oddly put out by the use of what was clearly a pet name. *Leo,* for heaven's sake!

Sue leaned forward. She knew quite as well as Jessica what a stumbling block local resistance to a new development could be. She said anxiously, 'But surely Prince Giorgio will have taken the local council or whatever along with him?' And, as Simone looked puzzled, translated with impatience, 'Got permission. Got their agreement.'

Leandro and his guest exchanged looks, then slowly Spinoletti shook his head.

'I can see you do not know the way my uncle works,' Leandro drawled. 'He does not normally waste time asking permission.'

'He does not need permission to build on his own land,' snapped Sandra suddenly, reaching for more wine.

'Ah, but is it his own land? I would say that was a moot point,' murmured Leandro.

Jessica threw him a startled look. She had not bothered to check the land title. It was not her job, for one thing, and for another she assumed that the Prince's legal advisers would know more about Italian law on land ownership than she did.

Sandra's hand appeared to be shaking. She said, in a strangled voice, 'He paid for it.'

Leandro did not answer. He merely allowed his eyebrows to flick towards his hairline in insolent disbelief.

'He did,' Sandra insisted. She gulped at her wine.

Here, thought Jessica, looking from one to the other in slight dismay, was a mystery and, more than that, a nuisance. She caught Sue's eye. It was plain that her secretary was thinking very much along the same lines.

'You're just being difficult,' Sandra said crossly. 'Trying to make trouble.'

'Now why should I do that?' He was soft as a cat's paw—and ten times as dangerous, Jessica judged.

'Because you're jealous of him,' Sandra snapped.

Then, as if she was suddenly startled into sobriety by what she had said, she sat back in her chair suddenly, looking rather white.

Leandro's eyes had narrowed, and once again Jessica was reminded how sharp those eyes could be when he was not play-acting.

'Jealous?' he mused. 'Now I find that very interesting. Why should I be jealous of my uncle, Sandra?'

But she said nothing, nursing her wine against her breast in a protective gesture, her mouth mulish.

'Why?'

Their eyes met and locked. Jessica had the strong impression that there was some unspoken conversation going on, perfectly intelligible to both parties involved but hidden from everyone else. She shifted uncomfortably.

The little scene was interrupted only by the arrival of Enrico, flanked by two manservants bearing silver trays of food.

Sue's eyes widened. Jessica looked across the table at her in amusement; she had felt exactly the same herself on her first evening. As the meal progressed at its normal stately pace and Sue's eyelids began to droop, Jessica's amusement was tempered with sympathy.

As soon as she reasonably could, she excused herself, declining cheese or any of the sticky pastries that the chef served to terminate the meal. Sue, in profound gratitude, followed her out.

'Phew!' she exclaimed when they were in the softly lit corridor. 'Is it always like that?'

'Like the Hapsburgs on a good evening?'

Sue nodded.

'More or less,' Jessica told her. 'I didn't believe it the first time I saw it. There was the Body Beautiful wearing nothing but jeans and medallions, and me in my travel stains, and Enrico went parading up and down the table between us as if it was the Coronation.'

Sue gave a sleepy giggle. 'I'd have given a lot to see that!'

Jessica said gloomily, 'Leandro thought it was amazingly funny.'

They were walking slowly down the corridor, their heels clicking on the parquet floor.

'He's nice, isn't he?' said Sue idly.

They turned a corner.

'No,' said Jessica with great calm. 'He's glamorous, gorgeous, and he has a nasty sense of humour. He is not nice.' She sent Sue a warning look. 'Very much not nice.'

Sue shrugged. 'You're thinking of the newspaper stories.'

With great restraint Jessica said, 'I'm thinking entirely of the way he's behaved since I arrived.'

Sue looked at her speculatively but refrained from asking the obvious question. It hung in the air between them, though, palpably the next step in the conversation. Jessica refused to respond to the unasked query, pacing beside Sue, her lips folded resolutely. Sue sighed.

'Is it so very dreadful that an attractive man should,' she hesitated, 'make up to you a little?'

They climbed a carpeted staircase, unlike anything Sue had ever seen on a boat before, and entered the corridor that Sue recognised, before Jessica answered. When she did, it was not to tell Sue to mind her own business, as she had half expected. Nor was she angry. She seemed, if anything, slightly puzzled.

'I know it must seem silly, but it unsettles me.' She stopped and turned to face Sue suddenly, her face disturbed. 'He makes me feel as if he's laughing at me all the time. As if he knows something I don't. I know he pays me compliments and you think he's flirting with me. Well, the staff all think he's flirting with me.' She fell silent.

'And that's so terrible?' prompted Sue.

'No,' said Jessica slowly. 'No, it wouldn't be, if that was all. But I have a feeling—oh, you'll say it's my paranoia, I know—but I feel as if it's all *aimed* at something.' She started to walk again, staring ahead, her expression unhappy. 'He makes me uneasy, Sue. I can't explain it better than that.'

Sue did not know what to say. She shook her head, sure that Jessica was over-suspicious and not knowing how to tell her so in the face of her obvious perturbation.

At last she said in a practical tone, 'Do you want to leave, then?'

Jessica was so deep in her thoughts, she almost jumped.

'Leave?' she echoed. 'Oh, no, I can't. I haven't finished.'

'You could finish in London,' Sue pointed out, suppressing a yawn.

Jessica shook her head. 'I'd have to keep coming back. It would be just as bad.'

'Maybe worse. At least if he's underfoot every day you'll get used to him,' observed Sue, failing to suppress the next yawn.

Jessica looked unconvinced but said no more, contenting herself with making sure that Sue had found her own cabin again, and bidding her goodnight.

Then she went slowly back to her own cabin, trying to shake off the feeling of unease with which the evening had left her. She felt like a player of a bit part who had arrived in the third act of a tragedy and had somehow, by dint of casual clues dropped by the protagonists, to pick up what was going on. Simone Spinoletti clearly had Prince Giorgio written down as the villain of the piece. Sandra defended him, but she did not seem very sure of her ground. And Leandro—where on earth did he stand? Was he accepting his uncle's hospitality while he tried to do a deal with his opponents behind his back?

Jessica frowned. That seemed out of character. She did not know how, but she was certain that Leandro would do whatever he intended to do out in the open, with no underhand skulduggery. Except perhaps in relation to herself.

Her frown grew blacker. She had the feeling that he was manipulating her. She did not know to what end and she did not know why. She was not even certain what she felt, beyond a deep, irrational instinct that told her Leandro regarded her as a puppet and that he pulled the strings.

She went into her state-room, pulling the door shut behind her with quite unnecessary vigour.

This time, at least, her papers had been left in the disarray into which she had sorted them. Jessica gave them a satisfied glance before crossing into the bedroom, where she sank on to the kidney-shaped stool in front of the dressing-table. The face in the mirror looked strained.

She passed a hand before her eyes. God, but she was tired! She was working hard, of course, but it was not that. Work invigorated her. Maybe the confines of the boat made her feel claustrophobic. Yes, maybe it was that. She was not used to having to summon a launch every time she wanted to leave the premises.

Jessica shook her head, ashamed. She could be honest in her thoughts, at least, she thought with a flicker of self-contempt. It was not the hothouse atmosphere of the

yacht, though she did not like it. It was not even driving
that hateful car of Leandro's, though it had taken all her
self-control to do so and she had been in a sweat of fear
by the time she reached the airport. She hoped Sue had
not detected it.

It was the man himself. He was the threat. She knew
he was a threat, had known from the first time she set
eyes on him.

'God help me,' she muttered, angry with herself, and
stood up, fiercely averting her eyes from the mirror
image.

That charm, those heart-throb looks, made him a
threat to all womankind. She was making a fuss about
nothing if she thought they were directed at her to any
specific purpose. And she had reason enough to take
evasive action. She must stop letting him get to her like
this. She must just stay calm, laugh at him a little when
she could not avoid him, and for the rest of the time simply keep out of his way.

She showered fast, fixing her thoughts firmly on
tomorrow's tasks. She took her make-up off with rapid
strokes, running an experimental hand over the skin of
her cheeks. It was warm. In spite of the cream Enrico
had found her she had caught the sun on her face and
shoulders. She would probably have an uncomfortable
night.

She shrugged philosophically, wrapping the light
towelling robe with Prince Giorgio's monogram on the
lapel round her as she went back to her room. She
paused. There was something different. Something
wrong?

She looked at the door. She had left it ajar, surely?
Now it was tight shut. She hesitated. Then, swallowing
hard, she went across to it and wrenched it open.

The outer cabin was still in disorder and quite empty.
Maybe the door had closed itself? She had got so used

to it that she no longer noticed, but the great yacht rocked gently all the time in the sea swell. Perhaps that movement had been sufficient to nudge the door shut?

And then her eye fell on the outer door into the corridor. It was open; only slightly, but it was distinctly open. She could see the faintly pink light from the corridor wall brackets.

Jessica went cold. She remembered, with total recall, the dull thud as she had closed that door. There was no possibility that it could have been swung open by anything short of a force-nine gale.

Her mouth went dry. For a moment she stood frozen in the middle of the floor, her eyes flying round the cabin again. She tied the belt of her robe, pulling it tight with fingers that shook slightly.

Then, summoning all her courage, she went to the corridor and looked out.

There was no one in the passageway. No other door was open. Sue's room, at the far end, seemed undisturbed. There were, Jessica knew, two empty cabins between herself and Sue and then a further cabin on the other side of her own. She turned towards that and, without warning, encountered a stunning blow.

She staggered, the world reeling before her eyes. Light seemed to blaze up and then extinguish suddenly, as if there had been an explosion. She heard a voice calling out in surprise, a flurry of banging doors, rushing feet, questions.

And at the same time, it seemed, there were strong hands on her body, laying her almost tenderly on the carpet before she was alone. She lost consciousness.

CHAPTER FOUR

THE world was swirling. Jessica was being pushed forward. Someone was pushing her hard, very fast. She was speeding down corridors so that their wall-bracketed lights ran into a blur, and all the time there was that insistent hand in the small of her back urging her to go faster.

She moaned.

'Lie still,' someone whispered.

Jessica turned her head towards the voice and the universe slowed a little.

'You're all right now.' That was the same voice.

She ventured to open her eyes. The world lurched to a stop, leaving her feeling slightly sick. The light was not bright, but it was oddly placed, she thought, so that she could only see the shadow of a shape.

'Chuck?' she said doubtfully.

There was a sharp movement. The light seemed to sway and flare. She closed her eyes again, turning her head into what she now realised was a pillow.

'Who is Chuck?' asked Leandro thoughtfully.

Jessica did not open her eyes, but she was now wide awake—wide awake and with a pounding headache. She knew how she had come by that headache, too. It had all come back to her; it came back as soon as Leandro spoke.

She kept her eyes tight shut, her brain working furiously.

'Who is Chuck?' he said again, and touched her face.

In spite of her wariness, her eyes flew open at that gentle caress. She found he was leaning over her. She could not read his expression. There was concern there, yes, but something else as well, something inflexible and rather frightening. She stared at him from the pillow, her eyes widening.

'So you're awake.' He straightened and then, to her consternation, sat on the side of the bed. She was, she saw, back in her own room. Somebody had placed her on top of the bedcovers and turned on the bedside lamp. Leandro?

She considered him cautiously. She could not forget those hands, breaking her fall. She was almost certain that had been Leandro. In which case, had he hit her as well? Because somebody certainly had. She put a hand to her temple and winced.

'You bumped your head,' Leandro told her.

She could read his expression now. It was very, very firm and faintly challenging. It chilled Jessica as nothing else about Leandro had ever done.

'What were you doing wandering about the corridor in my uncle's bathrobe?' he went on. He sounded amused, but his eyes, Jessica saw, stayed watchful. 'Dare I hope you were looking for me? No,' he gave a soft laugh, 'I thought not. Did you decide you wanted poor little Miss York to take midnight dictation?'

Jessica did not answer, simply staring up at him in gathering indignation. The indignation was tempered, however. Somebody had, after all, hit her hard enough to knock her out. She found she was just a little afraid.

Angry with herself and refusing to admit the fear, she levered herself up on her elbow.

'The door was open,' she said, not very lucidly. To her annoyance she sounded breathless and very shaken.

Leandro sent a quick, instinctive look over his shoulder.

'Door? Which door?'

'The door from my cabin into the passageway. I know I shut it.'

He said soothingly, 'You were dreaming.'

Jessica shook her head. Her hair had come down at some point and brushed her cheek in the movement. A hairgrip fell on to the bed.

'No, I wasn't asleep.' She swallowed. 'I was in the shower. When I came out, I——' She stopped. 'I thought I heard something,' she finished lamely.

His face darkened. 'Are you telling me that you went investigating noises on your own? Wrapped in a bathrobe? Have you no sense at all?'

Jessica was bewildered.

Seeing it, he calmed, saying with exaggerated patience, 'Did it not occur to you that an intruder might see that as an invitation?'

'It never even crossed my mind,' she said.

'You're a fool, then,' he informed her. 'But go on. You heard noises and the door was open. What them?'

'That's all. I was certain that I'd shut the door, so I went and looked out. . .'

He drew in his breath sharply but, when she paused, shook his head, saying nothing.

'There didn't seem to be anybody about. Then I turned, I think.' She frowned with the effort of remembering exactly. 'And somebody hit me. That's all.'

'Hit you?'

Mutely she touched the tender place above her right eye.

'You could have bumped into the door lintel, if you were tired. Still half asleep, perhaps.'

'You forget,' Jessica reminded him, 'I hadn't been asleep.'

'Oh.' He fell silent, his face unreadable. 'Why are you so sure somebody hit you, though? Did you see anyone?'

Slowly she shook her head. There was an unmistakable flare of relief in his eyes. She looked down at her fingers, not wanting to see it. But the mask was replaced before she looked away.

'If you're no more certain than that it might be a good idea not to go round announcing your suspicions,' Leandro said deliberately. 'It might worry people.'

Her eyes lifted then. He met and held them.

'Very well,' Jessica whispered, wondering why she felt near to tears.

He touched her face again, fleetingly.

'Don't look so worried. It won't happen again.' And when she did not reply he added fiercely, 'I give you my word.'

For some reason that only seemed to make it worse. Jessica swallowed a lump in her throat.

'Thank you,' she said.

He stood up. 'Do you want anything? A drink, perhaps? Something to make you sleep?'

'No.'

He paused, looking down at her. 'Try to put it out of your mind,' he said abruptly. 'I'm sure there is a reasonable explanation. Some mistake. . .'

'Yes,' she agreed. She sent him a quick upward look. 'I'm sure it was a mistake.' Her tone was dry.

He seemed to flinch for an instant. Then he smiled, that lazy devestating smile that for once she found she could not respond to.

'And I give you fair warning, Jessica *carissima;* if I find you wandering around in indiscreet bathrobes again, I won't be answerable for the consequences!'

He strolled to the door. Jessica smiled at the sally, but it was a forced smile. He looked back at her.

'There's just one thing I'd like to clear up. . .'

'Yes?' Her head was pounding now and she felt exhausted.

'Who is Chuck?' he asked, for the third time.

At another moment she would have told him to mind his own business; maybe she would have said that Chuck was another cynical heartbreaker like himself, so she had had her immunity dose. But she was too tired, too unhappy and too confused for a sharp retort. She made a small, eloquent gesture of her hands, revealing her helplessness, her inability to answer his question in a halfway rational manner.

Leandro's eyes narrowed. 'That important?'

'I——' Her voice broke. 'Look, I think I'm in shock. I'd like to go to sleep.'

He nodded, but not, she thought, at what she had said.

'You and I,' he said grimly, 'are due a long frank discussion.'

'Not now!' she protested with a kind of horror.

'No,' he agreed. 'No, I don't think either of us is up to it at the moment. But tomorrow I shall want a long talk. And if you barricade yourself in your room behind your plans and your secretary, I give you fair warning I shall carry you off by force.'

He smiled at her. But Jessica, with her forehead throbbing and her unwelcome suspicions, could not manage to smile back.

'Poor child,' he said then. 'You really are shaken, aren't you? Go to sleep, then.' He blew her a mischievous kiss. 'I'll see you in the morning.'

The next morning it all seemed like a dream. In fact, if it had not been for the soreness of her head, Jessica could have convinced herself that she had imagined the entire incident.

Nothing was missing from her papers; as far as she could see they had not even disturbed. None of the elegant furniture had been moved and the small wall-safe behind the ornate gilt mirror was untouched.

She sipped her coffee, mulling over the whole course of events. In the light of day it seemed ridiculous to suspect her host's nephew of having laid violent hands on her. For one thing he had no reason to; for another she did not think violence was his style. He was too lazy, too charming. If he wanted to get anything from her, information or advice against his uncle's interests, she was fairly sure he would try to woo it out of her first. And she was not at all sure that she had the strength of will to resist him, which annoyed her more than a little.

By the time Sue arrived, she was in a fair way to convincing herself that it had all been a mistake and she had somehow managed to knock herself out by turning unwarily into the door frame.

Sue, taking one look at the darkening bruise on her brow, commented, 'Goodness, plays rough, does he?'

'What?' Jessica looked up from her coffee.

Sue looked faintly uncomfortable. 'I'm afraid I—er—saw Leandro last night.'

Jessica stared at her. 'I don't follow. Last night? You mean after we left the dinner table?' She raised her eyebrows. 'Are you trying to tell me you've had a fling with the Body Beautiful?'

Sue snorted. 'Of course not. I mean I saw him here.'

'Here? In this room?'

'Well, coming out of this room, actually.' Sue poured her own coffee. 'I'm sorry, Jess. I wasn't spying, honestly. I thought I heard something. I padded around my cabin in a panic for a bit, then I stuck my nose out into the corridor and saw Leandro.'

'Ah.' Jessica put her cup down. 'Leaving my room. I see.'

'Er—yes,' said Sue, spooning sugar distractedly.

Jessica observed her with dispassionate eyes. 'You'll turn that into treacle if you're not careful. So you saw Leandro leaving my room and drew the obvious conclusions. Did he see you?'

'Oh yes.' Sue sipped her coffee, made a face at its sweetness, and sank on to a chair.

'And what did he say?'

Sue shook her head.

Jessica's mouth tightened. 'Do?' she asked, without much hope of it being anything that would salvage her reputation.

'Well he waved,' Sue said doubtfully. 'He seemed quite pleased with himself. But a bit preoccupied, if you know what I mean.

'I'll bet,' muttered Jessica. She said, 'Is there any point in me assuring you that I had an accident last night and he helped me?'

'Why him?' Sue asked simply. 'Why didn't you ring me or—or Enrico?

'Because he happened to be there.'

'Happened?' Sue allowed the question to convey all her amused suspicion.

But Jessica was not amused. It brought alive too vividly her own suspicions of the night before. Yes, Leandro had been there very conveniently, hadn't he? And he had not offered any explanation for his presence in the corridor, either. Jessica knew well enough that he had one of the master suites on the higher deck. There was no reason for him to penetrate to the level where she and Sue were staying.

'Hey, Jess, don't look like that! I told you, I don't blame you. He's a nice guy, and it's time you had a fling.'

Jessica put away her dark suspicions. There was nothing she could do about them, and he had given his word that it wouldn't happen again, hadn't he?

So she snorted and said with a return to her usual astringency, 'You ought to offer Leandro a deal—you do his public relations for him, he plies you with champagne at four in the afternoon.'

Sue grinned at the reference to their conversation of the day before.

'Well, I haven't had any yet,' she pointed out, though the look she gave Jessica was searching.

Jessica waved a hand at the bell push. 'Then summon Enrico and demand a whole new life experience,' she said.

'Champagne for *breakfast?*' Sue's voice was awed.

She had it, too. Admittedly it was mixed with freshly squeezed orange juice and flanked by hot sweet rolls, but Sue's expression was as bemused as if she had floated home at dawn to drink champagne in romantic bliss with the love of her life.

'I prefer egg and bacon, myself,' said Jessica, teasing her.

'Then why don't you have it?' asked Sue, lathering homemade plum jam on to a roll with enthusiasm.

'Because Enrico doesn't like bringing full breakfasts into the cabins. If I want to make a pig of myself I'm expected to go and do it formally at the table,' Jessica said candidly.

'So why. . .?' Sue stopped and put down her jammy handful. 'Leandro?' she asked with understanding. 'You don't want to have breakfast with Leandro.'

'Or any other meal if I can get out of it,' agreed Jessica.

Sue resumed eating. At length she said abruptly, 'How did you get that bruise? You didn't really have a fight, did you?'

'With the Body Beautiful?' Jessica hoped she sounded suitably disdainful. There was no reason for it, but she had the strongest urge to keep the exact details, and above all her unwilling suspicions, about last night to herself. 'Yes, of course.' She clasped her hands to her breast dramatically. 'He tried to seduce me and, when I resisted, struck me to the ground in his rage.'

'Oh, right,' said Sue placidly, clearly relieved. 'And then went home leaving you unseduced?'

'I have no idea where he went,' said Jessica loftily.

Sue laughed. 'Probably drowned himself, in the best tradition.'

Jessica sniffed. 'No such luck. He swims like a fish.'

'Yes, I suppose he would.' Sue contemplated the thought of their host's nephew for a few pleasurable seconds. 'Do you suppose there's anything he doesn't do superbly well?' she wondered, her voice just a little wistful.

'Yes,' snapped Jessica. 'Work.'

She was able to see the truth of her assertion within a few hours. She was returning from a light lunch on deck when she saw the launch approach. Leandro was standing behind the spray shield. He waved to her.

Reluctantly, Jessica went to the rail. It was odd, she thought, impatient with herself, the effect he had on her—as if she was compelled to obey his slightest whim, even when it was unvoiced.

She was wearing her most disagreeable face when he came up to her. Leandro duly took note of the fact.

'You're looking very sour,' he remarked in his most caressing tone. 'What have I done now?'

'Done?' Jessica gave him her most limpid smile. 'You? I didn't know you believed in doing things, Leandro.'

He gave a soft laugh. 'You know, when you are angry your eyes go bright green,' he said irrelevantly.

She shrugged, annoyed. It was perfectly true, she knew.

'Angry with me?'

She hunched a shoulder, turning away from him to look across the water to the little sheltered harbour. The sun turned the sea into a glimmering cluster of light. Beyond, the little town, with its ochre and rose paint and wooded embracing hills, looked unreal.

'Why?' he asked quietly, his hand just touching her bare arm.

She stood very still, like a mesmerised animal.

'I don't know.' It was not much more than a breath. 'Because you make me—I can't explain.'

'What do I make you do?' For once he was not playing the heavy romantic. He did not seem amused, either. He might almost have been serious.

Not looking at him, Jessica said in a rush, 'Do things.' She drummed her fists on the rail. 'Do things I don't want to do.'

'Jessica. . .' He turned her round into his arms. She was stiff, still angry, but she went.

He held her against him for a long moment. His skin was warm from the sun; she could feel his heart beating under her cheek. He said her name again, and she looked at him.

'What things you don't want to do?' he murmured, a smile in his voice. 'This?'

And kissed her. Jessica knew he was going to kiss her and did nothing to resist. She even reached up to him, her hands sliding round his neck as his head dipped and her eyes unfocused.

It was a surprisingly ungentle kiss. His hands were like steel bars on her shoulder blades and his teeth grazed the soft inner skin of her lip. He kissed her until she was breathless and then went on kissing her until she struggled away from him, gasping.

She held herself away from him, one hand braced against his chest, which was rising and falling deeply. Presumably, thought Jessica as sanity returned, he was as badly in need of air as she was herself.

She said wryly, 'Are you into suffocation, Leandro?'

His eyes danced. 'It has its compensations.'

She stepped back, one hand at her throat in a pantomime of relief. 'I can't say I see any.'

'You will,' he said, crinkling his eyes at her.

She smoothed her hair. 'You think?'

'I'd put money on it,' he said, with infuriating assurance.

She looked away from him. He was too attractive, damn him, and he knew it.

'I doubt it,' she said in her coolest tone. She surveyed him, now taking in that he was dressed relatively formally, with a blazer thrown over a crisp open-necked shirt, and impeccably creased dark trousers. 'Have you been to town?'

For a moment his eyes blanked, then he said, 'You saw me in the launch. You know I have been ashore.'

'Yes, but where. Portofino? Or the big city?'

He seemed to hesitate, then he said, 'I have been taking the car for a run. I felt like some speed.'

The opportunity to tease him in return for once was irresistible. 'Company on board a bit slow for you?' Jessica asked innocently.

His eyes gleamed. 'Not at all,' he said, and whirled her back into his arms and off her balance in one lightning movement.

'Let me go!' snapped Jessica, thoroughly annoyed.

But Leandro was enjoying himself. Her feet flailed. She caught a toe against the side of the boat and gave a squeak of pain and annoyance, but he ignored it.

At last Leandro lifted his head and laughed down at her. He was still holding her so that her toes were just off the ground. She tossed her hair back and glared at him.

'Oaf!' she snapped.

He set her down with exaggerated care. She shook her shoulders, smoothing her cotton skirt with fingers that she tried not to notice were shaking.

'Not at all.' He helped her straighten her skirt. Jessica could have hit him. 'I am simply reluctant to let a challenge go unanswered.'

'I'll bear that in mind,' she told him with feeling. 'No more challenges.'

The golden eyes laughed down at her. 'That,' he told her solemnly, 'would be a pity.'

It was unthinkable that this man could have hit her in the dark last night, surely? The little chilled question in the back of her mind surfaced again unbidden. Jessica shook her head, unaware that her eyes darkened unhappily.

'What's wrong?' asked Leandro, suddenly sober.

She gave him a swift, not very convincing smile.

'I'm not wild about being grabbed and swung in the air,' she said with a palpable effort.

'I'll grab you and throw you to the floor next time, then,' he promised lightly, but his eyes were searching. 'There is something more than that, though. Tell me.'

He must know, surely. Still. . .

Soberly, Jessica said, 'Last night.'

At once he was tense, still and tense like a fighter poised for combat. But his voice was silky. 'What about last night?'

'Why were you there? Just at the moment when. . .'

'When you had your accident,' he interrupted smoothly. 'But I wasn't. I came along and found you out cold. I don't know how long you had been lying there.'

And Jessica, remembering the hands which had broken her fall, had to accept that either her memory was at fault or he was not going to tell her the truth. She looked at him, searching his eyes for a clue, but there was nothing there.

She had a feeling, in her bones, that he was lying. She did not know why. It hurt, too, and she could not account for that, either.

She turned away. 'I must get back to work,' she said in a colourless voice.

'Wait.' He did not touch her but, as usual, she obeyed him, she thought wryly. 'We have not yet had our talk.'

'I have no time,' she said, not meeting his eyes. 'There's a lot to do.'

'Leave it till this evening when it is cooler.' His voice was an invitation in itself. 'Come and sunbathe for an hour and talk to me. We need some time together, I think.'

Jessica, who could think of very little that she needed less, gave a strangled laugh.

'That's not what I'm paid for.'

'Don't be prim. My uncle won't care.'

'*I* care,' she said obstinately, and backed away from him.

'Don't look so scared!' Leandro was amused. 'I promise not to jump on you again.' He threw his hands up in the air comically in mock surrender. 'Look, I give in. I only want to talk.'

'*No*,' said Jessica almost violently. It was addressed as much to herself as to him. 'I will not!'

She almost fled from him, down the companionway and back to her cabin where Sue, typing furiously, looked up in some surprise.

'There you are! I thought you'd got lost again. Prince Giorgio telephoned.'

'Oh, blast!' Jessica swung herself on to the desk and pounded her fists on her knee. 'I've been trying to get hold of him for days. Bother, bother, bother. Why did he have to call the one time I was away from the phone?'

'Well, it won't matter much,' Sue comforted her. 'He's coming aboard.'

'Really?' Jessica was astounded. The Prince had told her that he would not be returning to the yacht for several weeks, that she had the free run of it in his absence. 'Are you sure?'

'Positive. He says there's some trouble.'

Jessica swung her legs thoughtfully. 'Trouble? What sort of trouble? Difficulties about planning permission?'

Sue shook her head. 'Nothing to do with the project. He said it was personal.' She hesitated. 'He didn't sound too pleased.'

'Personal?'

For a moment Jessica's overactive conscience made her wonder whether the Prince disapproved of her sunbathing with his nephew as she had done yesterday. Then she caught herself. That was nonsensical. As Leandro said, his uncle would not care, even if he knew. And there was no one to tell him. She frowned.

Sue said, 'He said something about it being a family problem. I wondered—that is, I rather got the impression that—well, to be truthful, that he was annoyed.'

'Leandro,' said Jessica slowly. 'The adored nephew has dropped in the popularity ratings.'

Sue bent over her keyboard. 'That's what it sounded like,' she agreed.

'Now why do you suppose that is?' Jessica mused. 'Because he's lazing around doing nothing? Prince Giorgio must be used to that. Because he's flirting with the opposition? Maybe Prince Giorgio isn't keen on him inviting Spinoletti on board.'

'Or maybe because he's flirting with the architect?' murmured Sue.

Jessica nearly fell off her corner of the desk in outrage. Sue grinned at her.

'You're ridiculous,' Jessica said crossly, and took herself off to work in dignified—if slightly sulky—silence.

CHAPTER FIVE

PRINCE GIORGIO arrived before dinner. Jessica vaguely heard the commotion of his arrival and, when she went out into the corridor, saw a mountain of matching baggage being wheeled along. She was slightly surprised. Although the Prince was always dapper, she had not expected him to travel with such a volume of luggage.

When she arrived on deck for pre-dinner drinks, however, she saw she had been mistaken.

'May I introduce Miss Shelburne, Ida?' the Prince said to a tall lady. 'Miss Shelburne, my sister, Signora Volpi.'

Jessica murmured something, holding out her hand. For a moment, to her intense surprise, she thought it might be ignored, then Ida Volpi lifted a heavily beringed hand and just touched the ends of her fingers.

'You are working for my brother?' asked Signora Volpi in strongly accented English.

Jessica agreed that she was.

'You are lucky to be here on his boat,' was the next comment.

It might of course have been meant kindly and lost something in the *Signora's* evidently imperfect command of English. Jessica did not think so. She wondered whether the *Signora* was rude to employees on principle, or whether she particularly disliked foreign females.

'Young foreign females,' said Sue later. 'She's got a chip on her shoulder about being over fifty, apparently. And about being the poor relation.'

Jessica gave a little shiver. She knew all too clearly what it was like to be a poor relation and she pitied Sig-

nora Volpi sincerely if that was the case. She did not tell
Sue, however. That was part of her life so buried in the
past that nobody knew about it. It was even fading from
her mother's memory, or so she hoped.

So she said, 'She doesn't look poor. Maybe it depends
on your benchmark, though. I suppose in relation to her
brother she is hard up.'

She did not think any more about the matter. For one
thing it was none of her business, for another she really
was working flat out now. She had had an idea to solve
the acute drainage problems of one end of the site and
was furiously bent on calculation as a result.

She even managed to put Leandro out of her mind for
long stretches at a time.

He, however, sought her out eventually. Sue had gone
to Portofino in the launch the next afternoon, leaving
Jessica with slide rule and calculator, happily absorbed.
The door of the cabin opened without her noticing.

'Impressive,' said an amused voice.

Jessica jumped violently, displacing several files and a
sketch that had been balanced on top of them. He picked
them up courteously.

'I didn't mean to startle you out of your skin,' he said.
'You do throw yourself into your work, don't you?'

Jessica, remembering their last encounter and her all
too pliant response, thought it prudent to retire behind
a chair.

'That's what I'm paid for,' she reminded him coolly.

A look of annoyance crossed the handsome face. 'I
wish you'd stop talking like that. I don't give a damn
what you're paid for.'

'I'd noticed,' she agreed—and then added, perhaps
unwisely, 'I think your mother might not agree with you.'

Leandro's face darkened further. 'My mother,' he said
precisely, 'is a fool and a snob. I avoid her whenever possible. When not, I ignore most of what she says.'

Jessica was startled. There was real feeling in the cold voice. She felt embarrassed. She did not want to know about Leandro Volpi's feelings; it made him all too human. It made him seem like herself, or Sue. As long as he remained a glamorous, remote figure she could—just—resist him. If he came any closer, it might no longer be possible.

So she said hastily, 'Your mother was quite right to remind me that I'm here as an employee. The prevailing holiday atmosphere can be very distracting.'

Leandro showed his teeth. 'I have never managed to distract you,' he complained.

Prudently Jessica did not answer that, though he waited expectantly.

When she stayed resolutely silent he laughed. 'Coward,' he remarked. 'I suppose you won't come ashore with me either?'

'Certainly not,' said Jessica with more haste than was quite dignified.

Leandro shook his head sorrowfully, 'Not even when my uncle approves? Even orders it?'

Jessica's eyes narrowed. 'What are you talking about?'

'My uncle Giorgio,' said Leandro airily, 'thought it would be a good idea if I took you back to the site. He does not have the time himself. He was,' he added mischievously, 'grateful to me for offering.'

Jessica strove with herself. 'How good of you,' she said at last.

'Yes, I thought that,' he agreed, pleased with himself.

'Unfortunately, today is not convenient.'

'I thought my uncle was paying you to suit his convenience, not your own?' murmured Leandro.

Jessica could have hit him. She pressed her lips together to keep back a sharp retort, while Leandro watched her in not unsympathetic amusement.

At last he said, 'Come on, Jessica. You want to see the site again, you told him so. I heard you tell Sandra so, myself. And here's the ideal opportunity. I'll see you on deck in ten minutes.'

When he had gone, Jessica walked over to the wall and, with great precision, banged her fist against it. It served to relieve her feelings, but it also made her feel very childish. Why did he have this effect on her? Normally she was so calm, so in control of herself and her surroundings. Why did Leandro Volpi have the power to reduce her to inarticulate fury—and then make her do exactly what he had already decided she should do?

There was no point in seething, however. He thought it very funny, but all it did for Jessica was to make her lose her sense of proportion.

So she went and climbed into jeans and a workman-like shirt, pulling on stout sensible shoes for scrambling over uneven ground, and went sedately up to join him.

When she caught sight of him, her resolution nearly faltered. Of course, Sue and the others had taken the yacht's main launch. There must be others Jessica reasoned, but Leandro had elected to use the speedboat. For a moment her heart leaped into her throat and she stopped dead.

Then her courage reasserted itself. The speedboat was a vehicle like any other. It would only go at frightening speeds if it was driven in that way. All she had to do was indicate that she disliked speed and they would travel more moderately.

She was aware, though of continuing reluctance to tell Leandro Volpi of her fear of speed. It was too like giving a part of herself away.

She climbed down into the boat very slowly. They were, she saw, going alone. This time there was no engineer with them as there had been when Leandro challenged her to lap the bay.

He took her hand in a firm clasp and swung her into the seat beside him. He was wearing jeans like herself, but his shirt had been tied carelessly by the sleeves across his broad bare shoulders, and he was wearing dark glasses. He looked the essence of the Riviera socialite at play. He also looked devastating.

Jessica made great play of putting on her own sunglasses. Leandro grinned at her as he released the anchoring rope and they pulled slowly away from the big yacht.

There was a breeze on the open sea. Jessica shivered. Although Leandro appeared to be concentrating on the water in front of him, he noticed.

'Did you bring a sweater? The wind can get quite sharp.'

'Yes.' She fumbled in her shoulder bag and brought out a crocheted shawl; her mother had made it for her last Christmas. The familiar folds were welcome in this unfamiliar setting. She gathered it round her. 'What about you?'

He slanted a look down at her, his eyes hidden by the darkened glass.

'I'm used to it.'

Jessica was put out, she did not know why. 'Oh, of course.'

'Now what does that mean?' he murmured teasingly. 'It sounds like more disapproval.'

'I wouldn't dare,' she assured him. 'I'm terribly impressed when you're being macho.' She gave a fluttery and utterly false sigh.

Leandro gave one of his shouts of laughter. 'Yes, I can see you are,' he said.

The boat sped onward, bucking as it rounded the first point. Unconsciously, Jessica clenched her hands in her lap. Leandro handled the boat expertly, she could see that. He was unruffled by the boat's swoopings as it hit the cross swell, but for Jessica the sensation of high velocity was a torment.

She fixed her eyes on the splash screen, trying to ignore the horizon which appeared and disappeared with such unsettling motion.

'How long will it take us?' she asked in her best conversational tone. The palms of her hands were wet with sweat.

'To get to Castel San Giorgio?' Leandro considered. 'Half an hour, maybe.'

Half an hour. Dear God!

Jessica swallowed. 'Do you know it well?'

He shrugged. 'What is there to know? Half a dozen families. Maybe thirty houses. A road like a cycle track.'

'And one of the best beaches on the coast,' Jessica reminded him.

It was the beach that had attracted Prince Giorgio in the first place; the beach and, he had told her laughingly, the name of the village. The beach was a great swathe of sand set in granite cliffs. The village was perched above it, the houses and the vine terraces on the gentler upper slopes. There was a steep set of worn steps from the village down to the beach past an outcrop of infertile scrub on a sizeable plateau. It was there that Prince Giorgio intended to build his holiday complex.

Leandro grinned at her. 'The beach, of course, is wonderful. And up to now undiscovered. We used to go swimming there when I was a child. We would take a picnic and stay for the whole day, my father and I. My uncle too, sometimes.'

This was the first time Jessica had heard him mention his father. To take her mind off the heaving boat and her wildly hammering heart, she said at random, 'Does your father come from this area, then?'

'My father is dead,' Leandro said quietly.

'Oh!' She was shocked. 'I didn't realise. 'I'm sorry.'

'Don't be.' He stared ahead, the fine profile austere. 'He had a hard life and he was very tired. Though he was great fun right up to the end.'

Jessica was touched. 'You were close?'

'Eventually.'

She looked at him consideringly. His tone did not
encourage questions, but the remark seemed to invite
them. She was debating, when he took the boat in a wide
swirling sweep round another headland and she was
flung sideways against him. To her horrified eyes it
seemed as if the nose of the vessel was pointing vertically
to the sky. She clung to the arm she had been thrown
against.

'Sorry. I should have warned you.' Leandro spun the
little wheel in his hands. 'There's the bay, directly ahead.'

Jessica recognised it, though she had not previously
approached from the sea.

'It's beautiful,' she said, righting herself in a little
embarassment.

'There are wonderful little coves all down this coast.'
Leandro looked mischievous. 'I could show you one that
was even better. If you're brave enough?'

'Why?' demanded Jessica, not trusting that look.

'Well, you'd be marooned. At my mercy.' He leered
at her, laughing. 'It can only be reached from the water.
So if I bore you, there is nowhere to run to. You have to
wait until I decide to take the boat home.'

'Could we swim?' asked Jessica, not knowing how
wistful she sounded.

'All day, if you like,' Leandro assured her. He looked
down at her, his glasses glinting. 'Will you risk it?'

She looked at the bay ahead, the fishing boat on the
beach and the figures on the steps. Undoubtedly she
ought to vote for Castel San Giorgio and go and look at
the site, but the thought of an empty beach of warm sand
beckoned.

'I'll risk it,' she said quickly before conscience had time
to change her mind.

'Good girl,' murmured Leandro.

And the boat changed course.

The beach was everything he promised. The sand was almost silver. There were large flat rocks, black as coal, on which they lay to soak up the sun and on which Leandro spread out the provisions he had brought in the boat.

'Did you know you were going to kidnap me?' asked Jessica, eyeing his preparations with ruefulness.

'I knew I was going to try.' He was opening a bottle of wine which he had removed from an ice-packed Thermos. 'Swim now or later?'

'I haven't brought anything to swim in,' she protested.

He shrugged. 'So swim without.'

She shook her head. 'I wouldn't feel comfortable.'

Unexpectedly, he did not tease. 'Wear your ordinary underwear, then. It will dry quickly enough.'

That, she thought, was true. She said doubtfully, 'I don't swim very well. Is it deep?'

'I'll look after you,' Leandro assured her. 'No, it's not deep until you get out of the bay.'

Jessica smiled at him. 'A challenge and a promise all in one! How could I resist?'

He watched her for a moment, the handsome head flung back to survey her as she stood on the outcrop of rock above him. The dark glasses hid his expression, but Jessica had the impression that he was unwontedly serious.

But all he said was, 'Bear it in mind, then.'

They swam immediately. The sea struck cold at first, but in seconds Jessica had adjusted. She paddled happily in the margins, turning on to her back and drifting, the sun on her face. The water was astonishingly clear and she could see small fish darting in and out of the crevices in the cliff where it drove below the surface. Eventually she turned over again and stroked in a leisurely way back to the shore.

She stretched out on her rock, noticing that her daisy-sprinkled cotton underwear became virtually transparent when wet. It caused her a momentary qualm, but then she thought of the topless beauties on the sophisticated beaches that Leandro must be used to. He would only laugh at her if she made a fuss.

She leaned back on her rock and sank into a half doze, soothed by the lulling of the sea to her right and the sun on her closed eyelids. It was only when that sun was suddenly blocked that she, reluctantly, opened her eyes.

'You look very peaceful,' Leandro told her softly. He had removed his glasses and his eyes were narrowed against the sun. He had obviously just emerged from the sea. There were drops of water on his face and glistening chest and his hair was dark with it. He was smiling lazily down at her.

In the suddenly deafening silence, Jessica swallowed. Something in the core of her body clenched hard. Oh no! she thought.

Apparently unaware, Leandro perched on the rock at her feet, his arms round one bent knee. He shook his head and the water flew. Some of the drops sprinkled Jessica; they were icy on her warm skin.

'Don't,' she protested, laughing, turning her head away instinctively. If she treated him like any other friendly companion for an afternoon picnic, maybe that terrible instinctive clenching would relax. Carefully she eased herself into a sitting position.

'Then wake up and talk to me,' he retorted.

He poured wine and gave her a glass. Miraculously it was still cool.

'The paradise of modern technology,' Jessica said drily, trying to diffuse the atmosphere that only she seemed to be conscious of.

'Not at all,' said Leandro calmly. 'In the days before portable ice boxes, we used to bury the wine in the sea until we wanted to drink it. It worked just as well.' He raised his glass, toasting her silently.

Jessica responded reluctantly. Sun and sea and the cool wine were a potent combination, she knew. They set the scene for romance and she did not want it. She did not want it so strongly, she was almost afraid of it.

But Leandro was unaware of her reservations, apparently. He leaned back against the cliff, the picture of a man at peace with the world.

'Every time we came to this coast, I used to beg and beg my father to bring me here,' he said reminiscently. 'It was the one place I remember in my childhood where I was never hurt or unhappy. We never did anything very special. We would fish a bit, swim a bit, play football. . .' He sighed. 'And the magic always worked.' His eyes lifted suddenly. 'Do you feel like that, Jessica?'

She looked round her, carefully, aware that her heart was beginning to beat with the reverberation of a drum roll. She hoped he could not hear it.

'It is a lovely place, of course. . .'

He said impatiently, 'Not here. I mean for yourself. Do you have places where you are always happy?'

Jessica considered it. 'I'm not sure. I used to love my home and when it was sold I thought it was the end of the world. But it wasn't magic, not in the way you describe. I suppose it couldn't be if you lived there all the time. Magic places are only for visiting, I think.'

'I expect you're right.' He was watching her. 'Why was your home sold?'

Jessica almost jumped at the unexpectedness of the question.

'Oh, my father died.' He waited and she went on, not very easily because the memory still hurt. 'There were a lot of debts. His business had not been going very well. And he had a partner who. . .' She bit her lip. No, she was not going to tell Leandro that. It was too private and too painful. It would spoil the day if they got too unguarded with each other. Correct that, Jessica, she told herself: if *you* got too unguarded.

He asked softly, 'What happened?'

'There was a car crash. It was an accident.' She put her hand up to her throat. 'He was not very sensible about money and he hadn't really thought about providing for Mother and me. I suppose he didn't expect to die, poor love.'

Leandro reached out, without changing his posture otherwise, and took her hand. Jessica was startled. But he did nothing else, just held it in a loose, comforting clasp.

'Go on.'

It was surprisingly easy. 'My mother was very—well, she'd been protected all her life. She didn't really know very much about running things, or money. Uncle Richard, my father's partner, took it all over.'

'And?' he prompted, when she fell silent.

She shook her head. 'He cheated us,' she said brutally.

His fingers tightened, suddenly and painfully, on her own. But all he said was, 'How?'

She shrugged. 'Every way, really. We weren't as badly off as he said, though Daddy hadn't been very successful—that was true. And Uncle Richard set up companies to buy things—the house, the family portraits, the china—at what I am told were knockdown prices. He sold most of it again, developed the land; put the business back on its feet as a result.' She paused. 'He'd bought all my mother's shares by that time, of course,' she said drily. 'He told her it was an act of charity. I remember her crying with gratitude.'

Leandro said, 'Surely that was fraud? Could you not have prosecuted?'

Jessica gave him an incredulous look. 'Do you know how much it costs to prosecute someone in England?

Anyway, we didn't know for ages. Then some employee that he'd sacked came and told my mother all about it. She didn't believe it at first, but. . .'

'And she did *nothing?*'

Jessica shook her head. 'She just wanted to forget.' She hesitated, remembering all too vividly that dreadful week. 'You see, by that time she'd come to trust Uncle Richard. To rely on him.' She looked away, out at the silver mirror that was the Mediterranean. 'She was going to marry him.'

Leandro said very softly, 'Dear, sweet heaven.'

'Yes,' agreed Jessica.

'And how old were you?'

'When my father died? Eight.'

'No. When you found out about kind Uncle Richard.'

'Sixteen,' she said without expression.

He muttered obscenely under his breath. 'Presumably you trusted him as well. Were you fond of him?'

'Yes,' she said desolately.

He gave her a long look. 'So what happened? You didn't prosecute. Did you tell him what you knew?'

'My mother had to.' Jessica shuddered uncontrollably. 'He even admitted it. He said the end justified the means. He was going to make it up to us, after all. That was why he had proposed to my mother. He didn't want to marry at all really, but his conscience prompted him.' Her voice was savage.

Leandro reached out and pulled her into his arms as if he could no longer bear the story. Jessica turned her head into his shoulder, oddly comforted by the gesture.

He said in a measured tone, 'And then what?'

'Then nothing, really.' She settled into his arms so that her head was resting on his shoulder and upper arm, and looked into the cloudless sky. She shrugged. 'We were solvent by then, just about. I was doing all right at school. We had somewhere to live because my mother had got a job as a housekeeper to a family.'

'Your mother sent him away?'

'That's one way of putting it.' She gave a harsh laugh. 'He marched out, saying she was ungrateful, that he'd always looked after us.' The remembered fury rose briefly, then died. 'We never saw him again,' she said.

'What about your mother, though?'

'I suppose if I was feeling dramatic I'd say it destroyed her,' Jessica told him in an unemotional tone. 'She'd always been very gentle, you see, very generous. After Uncle Richard, she got suspicious of everyone. She used to look for underhand motives in anything anyone else did for us. Wrongly, of course. That was why. . .'

'Why?' asked Leandro softly when she stopped.

Jessica drew herself out of his arms. She had been going to say that that was why she had ignored her mother's warnings against Chuck. She was so used by then to the warped view that her mother held of the world that she had laughed at her dire predictions. But in the end her mother had been right.

She was not, she found, willing to tell Leandro anything at all about her own venture into incautious trust.

He was too acute. 'Did you travel the same path, then?'

She gave him a startled, unguarded look.

Answering it, he said coolly, 'Well, you clearly burnt your fingers somehow. I don't think you're silly enough to build all these barriers of yours on the basis of someone else's experience, no matter how bad your mother's was.'

Jessica drew even further away, veiling her eyes. Leandro watched her, his mouth wry.

'And you're not going to tell me, right?'

She said as coolly as she could manage, 'You're imagining things.'

There was a little silence. For an instant his face looked bleak, almost as if she had hurt him, which had to be nonsense. Leandro Volpi was a charming sophisticate who had seen her determined indifference to him as a challenge. He was perhaps kinder than she had expected. He certainly seemed more understanding. But that did not mean that Jessica was going to allow him any closer than he had already come, which was a great deal too close for comfort. What to him was a casual afternoon's conversation, a brief holiday affair, could turn into altogether something much more important for her. Reluctantly but with determined honesty, Jessica recognised the fact. He was too damned attractive and, no matter how much she wanted to be, she was not immune.

He said quietly, 'No. But if you don't want to tell, then I can't make you.' He was still holding her hand. He took it on to his knee now and turned it over, studying the small bones, the neat, unpolished nails. 'Will you tell me something else, then?'

Jessica was wary. 'What?'

'You don't have to if you don't want. It's a cheek, I know,' he said, not very clearly.

'What is it?'

He sighed and said heavily, as if he did not really want to ask but had no alternative, 'Are you a virgin, Jessica?'

She stared at his bent head. She felt suddenly cold and very frightened indeed, though she was not quite sure of what. As a prelude to seduction it was unthinkable, so whatever his reason for asking, she was certain it was not that. Leandro was neither clumsy not unsubtle. So why did she feel suddenly very specifically threatened?

She tore her hand away from his in a violent movement. She also—though she could not begin to guess why—told him the truth.

'No,' she said.

CHAPTER SIX

IT was very strange, thought Jessica, how he never did what you expected

After her defiant announcement there had been a little pause while Leandro watched her enigmatically. Then he simply changed the subject. He asked none of the obvious questions. Instead he began, calmly and unemotionally, to tell her about the local villages, their history, their customs, until eventually she was able to take her share of the conversation with reasonable composure.

Later they swam again and he lent her a mask and an air tube from the speedboat so that she could watch the fish underwater.

'I've always wanted to try scuba diving,' she said, as they emerged, pushing the sodden hair back from her face as she pulled off the mask.

'Then why haven't you?'

She grimaced. 'I told you—I don't swim well enough.'

Leandro considered that. 'You could improve. All it takes is practice.'

Jessica laughed. 'No time.'

He raised one eyebrow. 'All work and no play. . .'

She flung up a hand. 'Makes Jessica a dull girl—I know, I know. You don't have to lecture me, I hear it all day from Sue.'

'Miss York,' he said warmly, 'is a very sensible lady.'

'And I'm a dull one. Ah, well,' she sighed, sending him a naughty look under her lashes.

'I do not intend to tell you what you are,' Leandro informed her drily. 'Though it would be a great relief to my feelings, you would not find it flattering.'

She shook her head, scattering droplets over him, laughing.

'Did you bring me here to insult me, *signor?*' she demanded in mock outrage.

'I brought you here,' he said deliberately, 'to see if it was possible to deflect you from work for more than fifteen minutes at a time.' He disposed himself on his rock, reaching for his towel which he rolled up and placed behind his head. 'I am glad to see it can be done,' he said.

On this utterance, infuriating and unpredictable as always, he closed his eyes and gave every appearance of having drifted off to sleep. Balked, Jessica returned to her own rock and lay down.

It was unnerving, this feeling she had of his being so completely capricious. She never knew what he would say or do from one moment to the next. At one point she had been positive he was out to seduce her. Then it had seemed as if the whole thing was much more serious than that. And now he was ignoring her.

It would be nice, she thought wistfully, to shake him out of that annoying calm. On the other hand, it would probably both be difficult and involve some risk to herself. On the whole it was probably wiser to dream about it than to try to bring it about.

She floated off into a half sleep, involving pleasurable visions of Leandro wrong-footed and apologetic; even, though by then she knew she was dreaming indeed, humble.

He awoke her, arrogantly, by tapping her smartly on the shoulder.

'The light will be gone in an hour or so. If you really want to wander round my uncle's future playground we should be moving.'

Jessica had been fast asleep. She awoke with a jump, turned her head, and stared straight up into his eyes. He was so close that she could see images of herself in them, distorted by the curvature of his eye. Confused, she looked at him, not certain where she was.

Leandro looked amused. 'Time to go,' he reminded her.

Her lashes fluttered down and she gave a yawn. Then focusing properly, she opened her eyes again and looked at him very straightly, not speaking.

His mouth thinned. The look of amusement vanished. The eyes looked almost black and very intent.

Jessica whispered his name, making it a question. He was leaning towards her, supporting himself on one hand, the wrist so close to her head that she could hear the pulse in it. The beat was strong, rapid.

She knew he was going to kiss her. She knew she was virtually asking him to kiss her, for all her silence. Maybe even by her silence.

And he wanted to. Just for a moment she was absolutely sure of what he wanted, what he intended. She reached a hand out and touched his cheek lightly with the tips of her fingers.

Leandro swooped suddenly. His lips brushed hers, just once; she felt the touch of his tongue. And then, as her eyes closed and her lips parted, he moved, almost flinging himself away from her.

'No time for dalliance, *cara*,' he said in a light, hard tone. 'I'm not climbing down those bloody steps in the dark—we'd break our necks! Twenty minutes up the steps, half an hour looking round, ten minutes down again, and we go home with the sunset.'

Jessica sat up very slowly. She felt bewildered. More than that she felt bereft, as if he had torn something away from her that he had given her before.

She wound her hair into a knot at the base of her neck with fingers that were not entirely steady. Leandro was not looking at her; he was looking at the speedboat, half turned away from her. His chest, she saw suddenly, was rising and falling as if he had run a race. Her eyes flew to his face, but it was expressionless. He was even putting on his dark glasses, locking his eyes away behind that mask.

She stood up, brushing the light powdering of sand from her legs. Her thoughts scurried like caged mice. She had wanted him to kiss her. He must have known; he could not have avoided knowing. So why had he turned away?

She looked at him and away again, quickly, before he could catch her looking at him, in case that shaming hunger still showed on her face. He had rejected it, rejected her. Her mouth was dry.

In a high, strained voice, she said, 'Will it really take twenty minutes?'

He turned back to her then. Presumably he was relieved that she was not going to make a scene, Jessica thought. A little gust of anger shook her and then evaporated. She half turned away from him, pulling her clothes on fast, kneeling to tie her shoelaces.

'Depends how good you are at climbing uneven stone stairways.'

Was it her imagination, or did he sound constrained as well?

She stood up and walked towards him with resolution, giving him a defensive smile.

'I do a lot of clambering. It's part of the architectural course: muddy sites, roofs, lofts. I'm halfway to being a mountain goat after all these years!'

Was his answering smile an effort?

'Then I don't know how long it will take. I've never been up there with a lady goat before.'

They went across the shingly beach to the speedboat. He did not help her in. In fact, for the rest of the day he was scrupulous in not touching her—not when they disembarked at the larger beach, not when she stumbled on an uneven step, not even when they were back at the yacht and she was stiff and less than graceful in climbing aboard.

Jessica said nothing, but she noticed the way he refrained from touching her and was chilled by it.

Leandro himself said nothing that would explain it. He was his normal self, quirky, amusing, with that underpinning of self-mockery that was so attractive. Outwardly he seemed the same. Sue York, meeting them on deck, clearly saw nothing unusual.

'Have a good day?' she asked, strolling with Jessica back to her cabin.

Jessica was good at disguising her feelings. Over the years she had had plenty of practice.

'In parts,' she said lightly.

'Ah.' Sue was intrigued. 'Does that mean the dashing Leandro distracted you?'

'I was sidetracked to the extent of a swim,' Jessica admitted.

Sue laughed. 'Only a swim? He must be losing his grip! At least, if the stories I hear are true.'

There was an odd little pain in Jessica's chest, as if all her blood had been seeping back to her heart and was now squeezing it hard. But all she said was, 'Very probably.'

Jessica at last sat back with a sigh. She had been working without a break since the early hours of the morning and now it was finished. She surveyed the neat drawings, the pile of text that Sue had typed, with pardonable satisfaction.

'I think,' she announced, 'I am pleased with myself.'

Sue looked up from where she was edging punched paper into a file, and smiled.

'You have every reason.'

'Well, I think so.' Jessica arched back in her chair, stretching her arms up behind her.

'Tired?' asked Sue, closing the file with a decisive snap and transferring it to her pile.

'Mmm.' Jessica let her arms fall. 'Cramped more than anything,' she said ruefully.

'And hungry, I should think. Do you know you forgot to eat your lunch?'

Jessica looked guilty. 'I realised later. But I wasn't hungry, I wanted to get this done.'

Sue picked up another set of papers and began to punch holes at the binding edge. She gave every appearance of being absorbed in the task.

'Is that because the project is so fascinating? Or because you want to get away?'

Jessica was not deceived by the neutral tone. She grinned at Sue's downbent head.

'I've got a lot of work waiting for me in the office,' she said, equally neutrally.

Sue gave her a sharp look. 'You're running away,' she accused.

Jessica turned wide green eyes on her secretary. 'Running away? Why should I do that?'

'You know,' Sue said shrewdly.

But Jessica shook her head.

'Jess, the man's crazy about you,' Sue said impatiently. 'And he's gorgeous. Why won't you even give it a try?' She sounded despairing.

Jessica stood up. 'Because I don't choose to,' she said decisively.

Sue's lips tightened in evident disapproval, but she said nothing more. She knew there was no point in protesting further when Jessica spoke in that tone of voice.

Jessica ignored the subject, going on to discuss the circulation of the papers they had prepared.

'Send a copy to Andrew by airmail this afternoon, and another to the office under separate cover. I'll give one to Prince Giorgio in person when he comes back this evening.

Sue was making a list. 'And the others?'

Jessica surveyed the piled files doubtfully. 'He asked me for seven copies. I suppose the others must be for his partners. Maybe the lawyers; the local authority, of course.' She debated. 'Best give them to Sandra.'

Sue grimaced. The Italian girl had not exactly been unfriendly but her manner was strange and she had sometimes forgotten things Sue had asked her to do. Sue preferred not to ask her for help as a result.

'I suppose so,' she said reluctantly.

Jessica shrugged, though her expression was one of understanding. 'I know. But she's Prince Giorgio's secretary and he is the one who's paying the bills. Anyway,' she added with a laugh, 'she won't be able to lose a pile that high, no matter how hard she tries.'

'She seems to be able to lose an amazing amount,' Sue said drily, remembering one or two painful misunderstandings as a result of Sandra's apparently erratic memory. 'But I suppose you're right.' She made to pick up the files.

Jessica stopped her. 'They're too heavy. Ring for Enrico and ask him to lend you one of those wheeled trolley things they serve the drinks from at Leandro's orgies.'

'That's an idea.' Sue rang the bell. She gave Jessica a mischievous glance. 'And when were you at one of his orgies?'

Jessica frowned. 'I wasn't. But I've seen the things and Enrico told me that was what they were used for. I thought they looked as if they might come in handy some time.'

'The orgies?' Sue teased, and encountered a fulminating glance from Jessica.

Before she could take up arms against the accusation, however, there was a knock and Enrico appeared. He observed the tray of uneaten lunch immediately and directed a look of such reproach at Jessica that she, to Sue's great amusement, began to fidget.

Sue explained their need. Enrico listened attentively and then reluctantly shook his head.

'I am so sorry, Miss York, but it is not possible. Tonight the *Signora* has a party, a big party. Already the little rolling tables you speak of are prepared.'

'Oh,' said Sue, philosophical.

'Oh?' queried Jessica, suddenly suspicious. 'A party? A real Volpi-style party? A two-orchestra party?'

Enrico looked slightly taken aback and he looked at Sue for help. Sue met the question in his eyes with a shake of the head and a faint shrug, disclaiming all knowledge.

He said rather helplessly, 'It was arranged some time ago, *signorina*. There will be about two hundred guests.'

Jessica's eyes narrowed. 'Why wasn't I told?'

'Really, Jess,' expostulated Sue. 'You can't expect them to ask your permission to give a party on their own yacht!'

That stopped her. She bit her lip. 'No, I suppose not. But—' she directed her words at Enrico '—I think I could expect not to be kept kept in the dark, either.'

He avoided her eyes, manifestly uncomfortable. 'I would be happy to assist Miss York to deliver the files to Prince Giorgio's office,' he offered.

Jessica brushed it aside. 'He told you not to tell me, didn't he?'

'I have received no instruction on the matter from Prince Giorgio,' Enrico said fluently.

'Not him.' Jessica was not deceived. 'The Body Beautiful. The resident heart-throb. The last of the great party-givers!' She was so angry, she was nearly spitting the words out.

Sue said quickly, 'That's not fair, Jess. You can't expect Enrico to answer that sort of question. They're his employers, for God's sake!'

'I am not,' said Jessica, rather white about the mouth, 'being manoeuvred into going to one of Leandro's Riviera revels.'

Sue exchanged eloquent looks with Enrico. 'Fine. Whatever you say. I can't see that one party here or there matters myself, but that's your business. Go ashore for the evening, if it's so important to you. Only stop abusing poor Enrico and let me get these files delivered.'

Jessica made no answer. She sat down, watching Sue and Enrico gather up files as if she could not quite bring them into focus. Her face was tense. Sue watched her unobtrusively as she went about her work and realised with a slight shock that, without make-up, Jessica's face was showing strain. There were faint shadows under her eyes as if she was not sleeping properly and the eyes were pulled down at the corners. As Sue watched, Jessica's lids blinked twice, and she shook her head as if she were throwing off tiredness.

'I'm sorry,' she said. 'I don't know why I'm sitting here. I'll give you a hand.'

She did so, and within ten minutes the files were with Sandra. The blonde received them with uncharacteristic preparedness, putting them on two shelves that had been cleared ready for them in a security cupboard.

'They are highly confidential, no?' she asked.

'I suppose they are,' Jessica agreed. 'I certainly don't want any other firm of architects pinching my ideas, anyway.'

'Pinching?'

'She means stealing—thieving,' explained Sue, as the blonde frowned. 'She is joking,' she added in explanation.

'I see. A joke,' said Sandra.

'I doubt it,' muttered Sue, and Jessica rapidly extracted her from Sandra's office.

'Why does the woman annoy you so much?' she asked.

Sue shrugged. 'I don't know. Maybe it's just chemistry.' She gave a sudden chuckle. 'I think I'm allergic to peroxide!'

Jessica stopped dead, giving a great shout of laughter. 'Sue York, you're a cat!' And then, intrigued, 'Do you really think that hair is unnatural?'

Sue gave her a disbelieving look. 'Jessica! Do you mean to say you can't tell?' And, as Jessica shook her head, she concluded drily, 'The hair is about as natural as her fingernails—I don't think she was born with crimson claws either. I don't know how she can type with talons that length.'

'No,' Jessica agreed thoughtfully. 'Now you mention, it, I don't either.'

'Maybe she doesn't have to type. Maybe she's the sort of secretary who orders flowers and reminds the boss of the family's birthdays.'

'I would think Prince Giorgio was too busy for that to be satisfactory,' murmured Jessica. 'Of course. . .' Her voice trailed off.

Sue scented mystery. 'Yes?'

'She sometimes seems very close to the Body Beautiful,' said Jessica lightly. 'She calls him Leo,' she added after a pause, as Sue continued to look at her expectantly.

Sue stared. 'You think she keeps the job because she's having a fling with Leandro?'

'It's possible.'

'It's nonsense,' Sue said roundly. 'I'm surprised you should even give it a moment's thought. It is not,' she added with some emphasis, 'Leandro Volpi's style. Even I can see that.'

Jessica looked unconvinced, but all she said was, 'You may be right,' and, in spite of determined needling from

Sue she refused to discuss the subject of Sandra or Leandro Volpi any further.

She did, however, make instant and thorough plans to be off the boat before the unadvertised party began. Sue was surprised at the determination Jessica brought to it.

'You'd think you were trying to avoid attending your own execution,' she observed, when Jessica put the phone down after arranging to take the launch to Portofino at seven-thirty.

'Maybe I am,' said Jessica drily and, true to form, said no more.

She had avoided Leandro, deliberately and successfully, ever since their outing to the beach. It was all too obvious that there was some pull of attraction between them which could, if not resisted, upset the even tenor of her existence. To be fair, Jessica was fairly certain that Leandro wanted to resist it as much as she did; that had been clear from his manner to her on the return from the beach.

She did not really understand why, though. Of course, it might be that he had at last recognised what she had told him all along—that she had different habits and assumptions and their ways of life were utterly incompatible. She did not think that was the answer, though. He had had plenty of opportunity to recognise the truth of her argument for days before the trip to the beach.

No, Jessica was inclined to think it was something to do with that question of his, and her answer. It was ironic really. If ever there was a man who was not entitled to despise a woman for not being a virgin, it was Leandro. But it seemed that from the moment she answered his question he had lost all interest in her. She shrugged. It was just as well. Fighting him off was exhilarating, but it distracted her from her work and made the yacht an uncomfortable place to stay.

She did not admit, even in her most private thoughts, that the loss of him as a sparring partner was also disappointing. The zest had gone out of life, at least temporarily. She acknowledged the fact but assured herself that it was entirely because she was tired. She would get back her energy when she returned to London and had a break.

At a little before seven-thirty she went to the side of the boat where the launch was moored. The young uniformed sailor helped her aboard and cast a quick look at his watch.

'Do you have a tight schedule this evening?' Jessica asked idly.

'This evening, *signorina*?'

'For the party. Don't you have to ferry people backwards and forwards?'

'Oh, that.' He smiled. 'No. There are a couple of men in the port who do that. They are hired on such occasions. I will only help if they get too busy and then only if Signor Leandro says I may.'

Suddenly uneasy, Jessica queried, 'Signor Leandro? But surely he'll want you to fetch his guests before anything else?'

The young man grinned. 'Perhaps. But these are not his guests.'

'What?'

'This is Signora Volpi's party, *signorina*,' he told her, happily unaware of her consternation. 'Signor Leandro has told her he will not stay on board for it.'

He looked at his watch again.

Jessica began to realise, with a sense of numb inevitability, that her careful strategy had been for nothing. When they were hailed and Leandro swarmed down the ladder into the launch she was hardly even surprised.

'All right, Gianni,' he said, casting off the mooring rope and nodding at the young man. 'Let's go.'

The sailor started the engine as Leandro lowered himself to sit beside Jessica. She met his flashing smile with resignation.

'Good evening, Jessica. I have not seen you lately. Are you well?'

'Very well,' she said gloomily.

He laughed. 'And very bad-tempered!' He patted her hand. 'Never mind, *cara*. You can spend an enjoyable evening telling me off.'

'Why should I do that?' she asked, trying to sound cool.

His eyes danced. 'Because my strategy is better than yours and you don't like it,' he told her.

She ignored that. 'I meant why should I spend the evening with you?'

'Because I'm kidnapping you,' he said flippantly.

'I could walk away,' she objected.

He raised one eyebrow, looking at the sea all round them.

'When we land.'

'Then I might decide not to land,' he said outrageously, adding, 'And you don't swim very well, do you? You told me so yourself.'

Jessica gave him a far from admiring look, and he smiled.

'Much better to allow me to feed you and relieve your feelings by quarrelling with me,' he advised, and leant back with one arm loosely round her shoulders, the picture of ease.

Jessica told him what she thought of him. She told him at length and with precision. The young sailor stood rigidly not looking at them, but it was obvious from the painful concentration of his posture that he spoke enough English to understand what she was saying. That infuriated her too, adding acidity to her remarks, but it seemed to give Leandro even further cause for amusement.

'You are quite right,' he said, when she finished. 'It is a frightful thing to do, to take a girl out to dinner and to see the sunset.' He shook his head.

'I am not,' said Jessica in a stifled voice, 'a girl.'

'No?' He put his head on one side, quizzically. 'Maybe you're right. You could be a fury, mmm? An avenging angel? A witch?'

'Oh!' In childish temper she drummed her fists on her knees. 'I could tip you out of this boat!' she exclaimed.

'I don't think you could, my dear. But you're welcome to try.'

Jessica prudently put her hands behind her back as he turned to her invitingly.

'Don't tempt me,' she gritted between her teeth.

'I have every intention of tempting you. I think it could be highly amusing,' he said calmly.

'Leandro. . .'

'Yes?'

'Oh, you're impossible! Why can't you accept that I just want to go off and have a quite meal on my own for once?'

'Quite right. That's exactly what we're going to do.'

'But I'm not alone when I'm with you,' she pointed out in a wail.

'Ah.' Leandro turned to her and took her hand in a warm, firm clasp. 'You feel it too.'

It was no good. He was an expert tease, too quick-witted to withstand. Jessica tried and failed to resist. Her choke of laughter was quickly suppressed, but he heard it. He lounged back on the seat, smiling at her, retaining her hand.

She sighed. 'Do you ever fail to get your own way?'

'Far too often.' He slanted a look at her. 'Can I take it that that oblique remark means that you are not going to make a break for it the moment we land?'

Resignedly she shook her head.

'Amazing,' he murmured. 'Don't look like that, *cara*. You might even enjoy yourself.'

'I might,' she said without inflection.

He squeezed her fingers. 'Particularly if I let you push me into the sea, I suppose. Well, I don't think I'm prepared to go quite that far. But I will give you the best seafood on the coast.'

'Thank you,' said Jessica nastily.

Leandro gave a chuckle. 'Not like that. You say, "Thank you, Leandro darling. I can hardly wait." '

'Thank you, Leandro.' Jessica showed her teeth. *'Darling.'* And then, with a wistful look at the sea and the side of the boat, 'I can hardly wait.'

His shoulders shook. 'If you tip me overboard, I will take you with me,' he promised her. 'And then you will really be in my power.'

She sniffed. 'No more than I am now. And it would be worth it, just to see you ruffled.'

'Darling—' it was a wicked imitation of her own tone '—you ruffle me all the time without having to resort to violence.'

'No one would guess,' Jessica assured him.

'Oh yes.' He turned her hand and set his wrist against her fingers so she could feel the pulse there. 'Oh yes,' he said again softly.

Startled and suddenly uncomfortable, Jessica snatched her hand back. He let it go without protest. In fact he began to feel in his pocket for the inevitable dark glasses which she disliked so much.

'And everyone *has* guessed. Except you, I suppose.'

She swallowed. 'Don't be ridiculous,' she said sharply.

'It is ridiculous to find you attractive?' he asked, sliding the glasses on to his nose.

'Yes, of course it is, and you know it.'

'I know nothing of the kind. Explain it to me.'

She stared at him in frustration. 'We're entirely different.'

He nodded, his mouth quirking. 'One male, one female.'

Jessica ignored that. 'You don't take anything seriously!'

'And you take everything much too seriously,' Leandro said swiftly. 'I think you need me as therapy.'

'There you are!' she said triumphantly. 'You don't even deny it. You think I'm dull and boring.'

He gave a soft laugh. 'Kiss me, Jessica.'

'What?'

'Kiss me,' he invited, 'and see how dull and boring I think you are.'

There was a tense silence. She could not read his eyes because they were hidden by the smoked glass, but everything else about him proclaimed that he was enjoying himself enormously. At my expense, thought Jessica. She gave him a measuring look.

'I'll offer you a trade,' she said at last.

He sat up. 'Trade?'

'Mmm. Swap.' She allowed him a sophisticated smile. 'One kiss.'

Leandro said uneasily, 'I have a feeling I'm not going to like this. What do I have to pay for my kiss?'

Jessica opened her green eyes very wide. 'The chance to tip you into the Mediterranean,' she said sweetly.

There was a choked sound from the helmsman, and Leandro turned slightly to look at him.

'Now see what you've done—you've embarrassed poor Gianni. Really, you liberated women have no consideration for people with more subdued customs,' he said in reproof.

'I'm sorry.' There was no sincerity in her voice at all.

'So you should be.' He ran a hand through his hair. She watched fascinated at the ripples in the streaked golden brown, wondering how it would feel to the touch. 'And, provided I get my kiss first, I accept.'

'What?' This time she was really startled.

He gave her a kindly smile. 'Only, of course, I shall choose my moment to take it. Maybe when you're full of scallops and Ligurian wine you won't feel so combative.'

Jessica surveyed him in unflattering silence. He laughed again, holding out his hand imperatively, and she stared at it.

'Or have you lost your nerve?' he challenged softly.

She sat bolt upright. 'Of course not!'

'Then you've got yourself a deal.'

He flapped the hand again.

Slowly, reluctantly, Jessica put her own into it. She had the feeling that once again she had been outflanked by superior strategy. As they shook hands on the bargain, she had a little suspicion that this was yet another stage along the road to her own ultimate defeat.

CHAPTER SEVEN

THEY were eating, she found, in a hotel set high above a small bay, overlooking a waterfront of tall, ochre, plastered buildings. They had moored in the good-sized harbour and then walked along the pavement above the shingly beach. Leandro held her hand, lightly but proprietorially, all the way.

'Where are we?' Jessica asked, trying to ignore the sensation that his fingers aroused.

He looked amused. She was very nearly sure that he guessed what she was feeling and also that she was determined not to let him see it.

But all he said was, 'Camogli. Famous for its sunsets and its thirteenth-century apartment blocks.'

She was startled. 'Are you joking?'

He shook his head, indicating the buildings past which they were walking. They were six or seven storeys high, with façades decorated in orange and apricot and innumerable pairs of shutters.

'It looks like an Advent calendar,' said Jessica involuntarily, stopping to stare at the one at which he was pointing.

Leandro grinned. 'Is that the professional architect speaking?'

'I've never designed an Advent calendar,' she told him loftily, unable to drag her eyes away from the façade before her. Suddenly she narrowed her eyes and said suspiciously, 'Is that shutter at the top there real? It only looks painted on to me.'

Leandro was delighted. 'Aha! The professional eye.'

She turned to him. 'You mean it *is* painted on?'

'I should think a good fifth of them are,' he said with complete sangfroid.

She gasped, beginning to feel indignant. He had plainly prepared a trap for her; but he continued blandly.

'One of the best games in this area is to walk round the little towns identifying scene-painters' windows. I've been doing it since I was a child. Have you not noticed the *trompe l'oeil* windows in Portofino?'

'I'm ashamed to say that I haven't,' Jessica confessed.

'That's because you always rush through it with your head down,' Leandro told her tolerantly.

His fingers tightened and he gave her hand a little tug. Slowly she began to walk along the path again at his bidding.

'What do you mean?'

He gave her an exasperated, quizzical look. 'My dear Jessica, you must know what I mean.'

She shook her head. 'Truly, I don't. Except,' she added with a flash of mischief, 'you sound very disapproving.'

'I am.' He drew her hand through the crook of his elbow as if it was the most natural thing in the world. Her fingers twitched, trying to retreat, and he calmly covered them with his other hand. 'I am very disapproving indeed. As I have already pointed out to you.'

'Because I haven't done the tourist bit in Portofino?' Jessica's voice was incredulous.

'Because you haven't done anything but work anywhere. As long as I've known you.'

She flashed a startled upward glance at him. 'But. . .'

'Jessica,' he said very pleasantly, 'if you tell me that's what you're paid for one more time, I swear I will forget my fancy education, and smack you.'

'Oh.' Jessica digested this and found she believed him.

He went on, 'My uncle is no doubt a hard taskmaster. I don't care for the way he treats his staff a lot of the time.

But I do not believe, no matter how anxious he is to have this damned project up and running, that he told you to slap on a pair of blinkers and walk around like a zombie until the work was complete. Now did he?'

'I——No,' she agreed in a small voice.

'Right. So when you dive through Portofino with your head down, thinking of nothing but the next stage in your work schedule, it's entirely your own fault.'

'Entirely,' she agreed. Her tone was even, but her eyes were beginning to glint. By what right did he take her to task? By what right did he manhandle her along the seafront without so much as a token apology?

Unaware of brewing resistance, Leandro said, '*That's* what I disapprove of.'

'I see.'

Alerted perhaps by the expressionless voice, he tightened his grip on her arm. But it was too late. With one swift, strong tug Jessica disengaged herself and moved to put a safe distance between them.

'I'm glad to know that,' she said politely. 'It will be so useful—if I ever mind whether you disapprove of me or not.'

He did not appear in the slightest disconcerted. Instead he gave a soft laugh, as if he were really enjoying himself.

'I'm glad you see it that way,' he said, smiling. 'I'll let you have a list some time.'

Jessica so forgot herself as to stamp her foot. The paving stones were uneven and, as she was mid-stride at the time, she nearly lurched off balance as a result. To her fury Leandro, though he surveyed the action interestedly, made no attempt to assist her.

She righted herself, rather flushed.

'Tired?' he asked solicitously.

Jessica tried to keep hold of her anger but, as so often with this infuriating man, felt it slide away into laughter.

'No. Just letting my worse self get the better of me,' she admitted ruefully. She sent him a considering look.

'I've never met a man who made me lose my wig as quickly as you do! You must be very bad for my blood pressure.'

'And you, my dear, are very bad for mine,' he assured her with a chuckle.

She was certain he was going to reach for her hand again, and she avoided him neatly, sighing.

'I suppose I asked for that.'

Leandro laughed. She gave him a measuring look.

'Why do you keep trying to flirt with me?' she asked in tones of despair. 'It's pointless, and you know I don't like it.'

The dark glasses hid his eyes. The soft voice told her nothing.

'Ah, but *why* don't you like it?'

'Why? Well, because it's silly, I suppose,' said Jessica, momentarily floundering. 'It embarrasses me. It doesn't mean anything.'

'If it embarrasses you, it must mean something,' Leandro pointed out in an academic tone. 'Even if it's only that you're not used to flirting.'

'Well, that's true enough,' she agreed.

He took her hand again. 'And that also is something of which I disapprove,' he said with finality.

He was impossible! He was utterly impervious to her feelings, or even the conventions of ordinary good manners, Jessica decided. This time she did not try to detach her hand from those possessive fingers. There did not really seem much point.

They went to the hotel Leandro had indicated from the sea. It was a stiffish climb and Jessica was out of breath by the time they arrived on the geranium-strewn terrace. Leandro, by contrast, was annoyingly unperturbed, she saw.

She complained, 'It's very unfair that, with a lifestyle like yours, you should survive that Himalayan ascent unpuffed.' She put a hand to her side where a stitch was beginning to make itself felt.

He laughed half-heartedly.

'What do you mean, a lifestyle like mine? I lead a very healthy life.'

'Sunshine all day and champagne all night?' she asked drily, as she got her breath back.

'It's better than hunching over drawing boards and never getting either sunshine or champagne.'

'That's a matter of opinion,' said Jessica, preparing for battle, but she was interrupted.

They were recognised, it seemed. Not only recognised but expected. Leandro, as she was beginning to realise, laid his plans very carefully, for all he looked so laid back. She wondered when he had booked their table for dinner this evening. Probably as soon as his mother announced her plans for the party, she thought sourly. He would not, of course, think it necessary to invite Jessica. He would simply make it impossible for her to go anywhere else.

He was talking to the waiter in low-voiced conference. Jessica, ignored, looked about her.

The terrace was on the very edge of the cliff, so that, if you leaned over the restraining barrier, you looked straight down into the sea that was drumming against the rocks below them. She shivered a little, watching as the spray was flung high into the air. It was a potent reminder of the vulnerability of human blood and bone.

Behind her Leandro said sharply, 'Don't lean too far out!'

She drew back, looking over her shoulder at him. He looked oddly pale, although that might be an illusion caused by the dying daylight and those masking black lenses.

He came quickly up to her and drew her away from the side.

'You can get mesmerised,' he said shortly, 'looking down like that. This is a bad coast for accidents.'

'Not presumably from the terraces of luxury hotels, however,' retorted Jessica. She found she was slightly shaken by this uncharacteristic behaviour. 'It would hardly be good for business to have people tipping over into the sea. That barrier looks pretty solid to me.'

Leandro let out a long breath. Then it seemed as if he took charge of himself again and whatever had provoked him was either dismissed or put to the back of his mind. He gave her a charming smile.

'You're right, of course. This terrace is designed to give a front stalls view of the sunset, not for people to leap into the sea.'

But he nevertheless drew her away from the edge of the terrace and seated her at a small white ironwork table. There was a blue and white sun umbrella above them which he promptly retracted.

'Even your skin doesn't need protection from the sun at this time of day,' he remarked, seating himself beside her and sliding his arm along the back of her chair.

Jessica raised her eyebrows, looking pointedly at the arm. He gave her his most charming and least readable smile.

'We are going to watch the sunset,' he said blandly.

The bay was set out before them, the little town, with its promontory of castle and church, to their right. Even as Jessica watched, the sky began to fill with streaks of rose and apricot. Light fractured on the edge of the drifting clouds, throwing rainbows into the water.

'It's going to be a good one,' said Leandro with satisfaction, and he let his hand fall comfortably on to her shoulder.

Beside them a waiter appeared with a tall bottle and two glass flutes on a silver tray. Leandro cast a quick glance at the bottle and nodded professionally. The man put down the tray and glasses on the table and began to rip gold foil from the cork of the bottle.

'What. . .' began Jessica.

But Leandro forestalled her. 'Sun,' he murmured mischievously, with a gesture at the Technicolor sky, 'champagne. . .'

Jessica watched, flinching slightly, as the waiter untwisted wire from the cork and then removed the cork itself with a great flourish and explosion of sound and wine.

Leandro shook his head deprecatingly. 'He must have shaken it up deliberately,' he told her. 'Removing a champagne cork is a simple business. One day I will show you. You do not need to sound as if you are opening World War Three. Nor do you need to waste the wine like that.'

'I'm sure you're an expert,' said Jessica.

'I am,' he agreed, oblivious of insult.

The waiter, slightly shamefaced, mopped the table and glasses, as well as the neck of the bottle, before putting the bottle in a free-standing ice bucket which he placed at Leandro's elbow. Then he put the glasses on the tray and offered one first to Jessica, then to her host.

Sighing, Jessica accepted hers.

'Leandro, are you trying to overwhelm me?' she asked, trying to sound amused and managing only to sound wary.

'No. I rely on the sunset to do that.' He gave a soft laugh at her expression. 'Poor Jessica! Don't look so outraged. Drink your champagne and abandon yourself to the beauties of nature.'

Disturbed, she did as he said. The sunset was certainly spectacular and, apart from that ominous arm about her shoulders, his behaviour was quite unthreatening. So why am I so jumpy? thought Jessica, bewildered.

She lifted her glass to her lips, pretending to drink, pretending to be absorbed in the expanse of sea and sky.

But in truth all she was aware of was Leandro: his steady breathing beside her, the warmth of his body, his eyes which, though they were hidden behind smoked glass, she knew never left her. Somewhere deep inside her she was aware of a trembling. It was a sensation of absolute weakness, almost as if she was ill or very afraid, and yet it was not unpleasant. It terrified her, so that she could hardly bear to sit still there beside him and watch the evening die.

They were not alone. Quite apart from the waiters, more and more people were drifting out on to the terrace to watch the sunset. There was a soft buzz of conversation. It was all very civilised and indolent. A number of their companions on the terrace were in evening dress, and one or two of them greeted Leandro casually.

Watching one of them, a tall woman with diamonds in her hair and ears, stroll away, Jessica murmured drily, 'The beauties of nature? The clink of ice in Martinis and the scent of Patou?'

She thought it would annoy him. She thought he would frown and call her a puritan as he had done before. But she misread him. He laughed.

'Close your eyes and enjoy it,' he advised. 'I'll wake you when the floor show starts.'

Jessica was so annoyed at this flippancy that she tossed off her glassful of champagne as if it was lemonade.

'I thought it had started,' she said, with a gesture at the sky.

He shook his head. 'You ain't seen nothing yet.' He reached round and poured more champagne into her glass.

The shadows were lengthening rapidly on the water-front path. A slight breeze had sprung up, stirring the leaves in the potted lemon trees on the terrace, and making the fringe of an awning on one of the buildings below them ripple. The sea, too, seemed to surge more strongly.

The clouds were moving fast now, breaking the bars of light as if they were beams from arc lights. It dazzled the eyes. Briefly Jessica wished she too were wearing dark glasses, much as she detested them on Leandro.

She said suddenly, not looking at him, 'Why do you wear those ridiculous sunglasses? They make you look like a Mafia hit man.'

Pained, Leandro said, 'Surely not? I am too fair—and besides, I dress too well.'

'Oh, they're designer sunglasses, are they?' demanded Jessica waspishly.

'I imagine someone designed them, certainly,' Leandro agreed at his most equable.

She cast him a look verging on dislike. 'They're an affectation. A silly, pointless affectation. Like champagne and all that sunbathing—good for the image.'

His mouth twisted a little. 'You don't like my image, do you, Jessica?'

'I don't have to like it,' she said, remembering her manners and scenting a challenge in one unnerving moment. 'It's nothing to do with me.'

'And if I told you. . .'

But she was not to find out what he might tell her. All around them the desultory conversation sank and a sigh went up. Startled, Jessica turned back to the vista—and gasped.

The clouds had now chased themselves out to sea and the sky was clear. The sun was an enormous disc the colour of fire and the whole sky and sea were bathed in the glow. The water below them looked like a cauldron of fire; even the foam was pink. The little town turned a burning rose. The buildings were suffused with it, the flagstones gleamed with it.

Jessica held her breath; everyone else on the terrace seemed to do the same. The clink of glasses and bottles was silent. Nobody spoke.

Slowly, slowly, the sun sank and the glorious mantle of colour turned from flame to orange to gold. And then, as Jessica thought it could not possibly be any more beautiful than it had been, it turned to the deep true burnished gold of ceremony. Against it the shadows were very black. The sun itself had slipped below the horizon and the sky was paler than the golden harbour, where little boats bobbed like jewels against their midnight shadows.

High in the sky, insubstantial as gossamer, a lemony moon appeared.

A long sigh went up from the terrace. Jessica found that Leandro had taken her hand and was holding it hard. She turned to him, eyes shining.

'Yes,' he said, and leaning forward, kissed her briefly but with decision.

On the terrace, normal communication was being resumed. Bottles were circulating, a woman laughed, someone called out to a waiter. In the almost dark Jessica and Leandro sat, not saying anything.

At last he moved.

'I wanted you to see that,' he said. His tone was abrupt, even awkward. 'It's famous, of course. But tonight was special.'

'I'm glad,' Jessica said simply. She turned her hand in his and her fingers returned his pressure. 'Thank you.'

She gave a little shiver of pleasure, and he saw it.

'Are you cold?'

'No.'

'You must say if you are. I told them I wanted us to eat out here, but if you want to go in. . .'

'No, I'm perfectly warm. As you pointed out yourself, I'm used to lower temperatures than you favour.'

'You are indeed.' His answer was amused and returned to the faintly teasing tone she had become accustomed to. 'Even so, it's late in the season and there is a breeze.'

'If I get cold you can be immensely macho and lend me your jacket,' Jessica told him calmly. 'I'd rather eat out here under the stars—truly.'

The arm about her shoulders gave her a quick hug. 'So there is some romance in your soul, after all.'

'Not a drop,' she retorted. 'But if I sit in the dark nobody will notice that I'm not a beautiful jetsetter wreathed in diamonds.'

His shoulders began to shake—she saw the movement in the darkness—but when he spoke he sounded solemn enough.

'Oh, Jessica, you will break my heart. So lovely and so cynical!'

'And so dowdy. And so bad for your image,' she added tranquilly.

The twilight was nearly over now, the last streaks of amber disappearing from the sky. Attendants began bringing lights from the hotel on to the terrace. They intensified the shadows where their illumination did not fall.

Leandro said slowly, 'Ah, yes, my image. I think we need to talk about that.'

A bracket containing four candles in glass shades stood at the edge of the terrace beside their table. Jessica looked up curiously, but behind the glasses his expression was unreadable.

'What's wrong with your image?' she asked flippantly.

'You tell me.' He was wry. 'You don't seem to care for it.'

She managed a little shrug. 'I suppose you're just not my type.'

'Or my image isn't.'

'There's a difference?'

'Oh yes,' said Leandro grimly. 'I'm not quite the shallow playboy you like to think.'

She was taken aback. 'I don't. . .'

'Don't you?' Suddenly and unexpectedly he grew savage. He smashed his fist down on the iron table so that the glasses jumped and a little of her wine spilled. 'Then why have you been needling me ever since you arrived on the yacht?' He started to mimic her primmest tones. ' "All that lazing about: don't you ever do a stroke of work? No honest man ever had a tan like that." You just took one look at me and decided I was not worth the time of day. And you and I both know why.'

Jessica said stiffly, 'It never occurred to me that a man with your reputation would want me to pass the time of day with him.'

His smile was twisted. 'You know exactly how much I want you, Jessica Shelburne, so you can stop lying about that for a start.'

She gasped. 'You're talking nonsense!'

'No, I'm not.'

She was lost, floundering. 'You can't possibly want. . . I mean, it's ridiculous. . .'

'Because of my reputation?' Leandro sounded weary. 'Jessica, why don't you drop your prejudices and *think* for a moment?'

'Think about what?'

'You and me. Us. The pair of us,' he added deliberately.

Jessica recoiled as if some of the hot wax from the candles beside her had spat on to her skin. 'We are not a pair!' she snapped in a fury of panic.

Leandro leaned forward and took both her hands in his, holding them firmly on the table. They were still side by side and his shoulder was strong against her own. Jessica felt trepidation touch her again, light and shivery as a moth's wing.

He said very quietly, without any of that teasing flirtation which she had learned to parry, 'I think you're wrong. We have been—' he hesitated '—attracted from the start. Both of us.'

'Attraction is not unique,' said Jessica in a stifled voice. 'I'm attracted to lots of men.'

'Do you scratch at all of them the way you have at me?'

'I——' She paused, disconcerted. 'No,' she said at last. Then, rallying, 'But you're a special case.' Her voice grew wry. 'They're not often international heartbreakers.'

He gave a sharp sigh and struck the table impatiently with their clasped hands.

'Look,' he said, 'when I was eighteen and had just left school, Giorgio took me under his wing. It lasted for a year. OK, I admit I did all the things you disapprove of, all the things that got my name in the papers and my photographs in the magazines. But it was nearly twenty years ago, for God's sake!'

'Are you trying to tell me that these days you're an upright citizen without an all-night party to your name?' Jessica asked drily.

Leandro laughed. 'I'm trying to tell you I grew up years ago. And I can think of something better to do with my nights than party.'

'I don't doubt that. It's what keeps your name in the papers twenty years on,' she pointed out.

He groaned, letting go her hand and pushing himself back in his chair.

'What can I say to convince you?' He sounded half amused, half despairing. 'Do you know the way these gossip-column types work? Here in Italy, at least.'

Jessica shook her head.

'Well, to a great extent they're invited to things by people who like the publicity—my uncle, my mother, people like that.'

'Not you?'

He shook his head. 'It's a damned nuisance. And sometimes worse than that.' His face darkened. 'Sometimes it's damaging, really damaging. It turns people into products so that people they've never met think they know all about them instantly. It's crazy! In the end, people like Giorgio don't know who they are any more; they just know the product requirements.'

Jessica could see the force of that, but she was still sceptical.

'And you've avoided it? But there's a file of press clippings on you. I saw some in England, and Enrico has a whole book of them.'

'Enrico,' said Leandro, 'has a nasty sense of humour. He has known me since I was six. He thought my year of wine, women and song was a deplorable waste of time and told me so. He also collected all the evidence so that he could taunt me about it ever after.'

'Recent press clippings,' said Jessica. 'For instance, you were in Paris at Christmas and. . .'

'At a dance of my mother's,' Leandro interrupted. 'She invited the columnists. I was there,' he shrugged, 'that's all.'

Jessica narrowed her eyes. 'They're interested in you just because you happen to be there?' She shook her head, 'I'm sorry, but I can't swallow that. There must have been hundreds of people there.'

'Yes, I concede that. But they knew me. Look—' he spread his hands '—a long time ago I sowed a few wild oats. They started a file on me; I'm in their card index. It's easy enough to keep it up, I suppose. I'm only on the fringe, but I do go to my mother's receptions. To Giorgio's parties, too, sometimes.' His face darkened briefly. 'I'm not important and they don't pursue me, but if there is nothing very much worth reporting, I'm good for a couple of column inches. That's all there is. I swear it.'

Almost against her better judgment, Jessica found she believed him. She said nothing but, from the way Leandro relaxed in his chair, she detected that he realised he had won his point. It was faintly annoying to be so transparent.

She moved slightly away from him, disengaging her hands. He did not try to recapture them. At that moment a waiter arrived with two enormous menus. Jessica hid behind hers as if it was a shield, but Leandro barely glanced at his. He obviously knew the bill of fare by heart, thought Jessica with a return to waspishness. He might not be the playboy she had at first thought him, but he was still a good deal more sophisticated than most of the other men she had known.

He said, 'Is there anything you particularly want to eat? Or shall I order for you?'

'You know everything on the menu?' she asked in dulcet tones.

Leandro looked amused. 'Still listing evidence of my misspent life? No, I haven't eaten my way through the menu and back. They just happen to have a convention here whereby they prepare their own specialities daily. I usually eat what the waiters recommend.' He gave her an ironic look. 'I thought you might like to do the same.'

Jessica had the grace to feel ashamed. 'I'm sorry.'

'Well, that's a step in the right direction.' He took the menu away from her. 'So what do you want?'

She bit her lip. 'Today's specialities, I suppose.'

'Good girl!' he approved, the laughter in his voice undisguised.

After that he began to talk to her in his most entertaining, lighthearted style. In spite of herself, Jessica felt exhilarated. It was as if, just for an evening, he was allowing her to taste the glitter and fun that he was habitually accustomed to. She did not really approve of it, but it was stimulating to sit opposite the most handsome man in the place and be teased and flirted with as if she were a princess.

Eventually she sat back, laughing at something he said. 'I feel like Cinderella,' she told him, unguardedly.

He raised his eyebrows. 'Feet hurt?'

'What?' she said, not following him.

'The glass footwear,' he explained.

'Oh!' She went off into a bubble of laughter. 'No, not that.'

'What, then?'

'Oh, as if I'm in a fairytale. Time out of the real world.'

Unexpectedly Leandro did not laugh. 'And it all ends at midnight?'

'Naturally.'

'Jessica——' He put his head on one side, considering her. 'Why do you have so little confidence?'

She was surprised and slightly affronted. 'I have bags of confidence. I'm a professional woman and I run my career and my life very satisfactorily. I wouldn't do that if I didn't have confidence in myself.'

'I don't think I meant self-confidence,' Leandro said thoughtfully. 'I meant confidence in things. Situations. Other people, maybe. You don't have any belief in anything except what you engineer yourself. I find it very difficult to deal with.'

Jessica stared at him. 'I don't follow.'

'No? Well then, tell me why this has to finish at midnight,' he challenged.

She surveyed him calmly. She had been enjoying herself so much that she had forgotten where this dangerous charm would lead her. It was inexcusable. He had never made any secret, after all, of his ultimate intentions with regard to herself.

She said coolly, 'Because I don't want to sleep with you.'

'Granted,' he said, apparently unmoved. 'Does that mean we have to stop talking as well?'

'You want to talk to me?'

'Don't sound so unbelieving,' he murmured. 'Though I admit I'd rather you talked to me.'

Jessica was instantly suspicious. 'What about?'

The glasses glinted. 'Who is Chuck?' asked Leandro mildly.

She choked. Whatever she had expected, it had not been that. He had caught her utterly off guard and it showed in her face. Leandro watched her thoughtfully.

'The reason you don't trust anyone but yourself, huh?'

She said, 'How did you. . .'

'You may have forgotten, but you once called me Chuck.' His mouth thinned. 'I've been wondering about the man ever since.'

Jessica averted her eyes. Beyond the terrace the Mediterranean was slapping softly against unseen rocks. It was odd, she thought, how in all that darkness, when it was impossible to see things, it was nevertheless obvious that the great sea beast was moving. She shivered a little.

'Was it a long time ago?' he prompted when she did not speak.

She turned back to him with an effort. 'I wasn't a teenager, if that's what you mean. I was old enough to know better.'

She was unprepared for the bitterness in her own voice. It slightly shocked her. Leandro, however, sounded completely unshocked.

'Aren't we all?' he said drily. 'What happened?'

She gave a slight shrug. 'Nothing very dramatic. Or very unusual, I imagine. You've probably done it yourself in your time.'

He made a sharp movement, quickly stilled. 'Tell,' he urged softly.

'Oh, it was a simple case of misunderstanding. He was in London working in the London office of his father's company. It was a temporary thing. What I believe is called a familiarisation visit.' She swallowed. 'I didn't know that.'

'You thought he was there for good? With you?' Leandro's tone was neutral.

Jessica smiled in the darkness. 'Well, maybe not for good. But for more than a few weeks, anyway.'

'A few weeks?' It ripped out at her. 'What happened?'

'I fell in love,' she said flatly. 'He was very charming. Life had been a bit grim, what with the money and my mother's broken engagement to Richard. Chuck was fun. He made me laugh. And he seemed—' she swallowed '—to care.'

'And?'

She shrugged again. 'He moved in. We were very happy.' She corrected it. '*I* was very happy. I lived in a shared house. He simply took over half my room. He got on well with everyone else in the house. We. . .' She swallowed again. This time she had to clear her throat. 'We used to travel to work together, even. And then we were on the tube one day in the morning. It was rush hour and we kept being thrown against each other. We were laughing like schoolchildren. And all of a sudden he said, "I'll miss this".'

Leandro made an inarticulate noise.

Jessica looked out to sea. 'He'd had a letter from his father—that morning, I suppose. He'd done well, and he was getting the promotion he wanted. He was going—I forget where. Somewhere in California, anyway. Where he wanted to go. Where he'd always wanted to go. He seemed quite surprised that I didn't know. He was sure he'd told me.'

'Oh, love,' said Leandro softly, reaching for her.

It was oddly comforting to lean against him.

'I didn't have to pretend for very long. He only had a week to pack and go—these American companies move fast.'

The hand about her shoulders was stroking her hair, very lightly.

'Why did you have to pretend?'

She gave a choked laugh. 'It had all been so public. Everyone was involved—people at work, the people I shared the house with. I couldn't just collapse.'

'Why not?'

She sighed. 'Pride, I suppose.' She thought for a moment. 'And a certain amount of vicarious experience. Collapsing hadn't done my mother any good.'

'And nor had trusting friends,' said Leandro, startling her with his perspicacity. 'I think I'm beginning to see. . .'

'Fortunately I'd nearly finished my training. It was quite easy to move. And then, after I'd qualified, Andrew wanted me to go into partnership with him and I got away from that side of the business altogether. I've never seen Chuck again.'

Leandro said, 'Are you still in love with him?'

Jessica's laugh broke. 'I don't know. Sometimes I still hate him. That doesn't seem like indifference, does it?'

'No,' said Leandro heavily. 'No, it doesn't.'

It was a temptation to continue leaning against that warm and friendly shoulder. Sternly Jessica resisted it.

'So now you know the full horror story. I told you it wasn't very spectacular,' she said, straightening.

'You also told me I'd probably done the same in my time,' he reminded her sharply. 'Let me clear that one up now. I have never in my life moved in with a girl. And I have never started a love affair on the basis of a field trip to a strange town. It's not my style.'

'I'm sorry.' Jessica could sense that he was very angry and realised that maybe she had given him cause. 'I shouldn't have said that.'

'No, you shouldn't. But it was probably just as well you did.' He leaned forward. 'Do you fall for the same man over and over again? Is that what you are afraid of? Have they all been carbon copies of Chuck?'

'No.'

'But they have all let you down?' he persisted.

'There hasn't been anyone else,' said Jessica, goaded. 'Once was more than enough.'

'*What?*' That really did seem to shock him as none of her earlier revelations had done. He sat staring at her.

'I suppose I'm what they call a one-man woman,' she said trying to sound uncaring.

'I don't believe that,' Leandro said almost violently.

'Don't you? Well, that's where the evidence seems to come down at the moment.'

'Why do you talk like that? As if it doesn't matter?'

'Because I don't suppose it does. Not in the overall scheme of things,' Jessica told him.

'Not even in the pattern of your own life?' Leandro asked swiftly.

'I think that was set a long time ago,' she answered soberly. 'There's not much I can do about it.'

'Oh, I have no patience with that defeatist attitude. You're as bad as Sandra. Of course there is something you can do about it.'

'Sandra?' Jessica was intrigued at this careless reference, but her question was prompted as much by the desire to distract him from her own affairs as interest in Prince Giorgio's secretary.

Leandro hesitated. 'Yes. She too has managed to convince herself that she is a one-man woman.'

And was the man Leandro? thought Jessica, aware of a small pain in the region of her heart for which there was absolutely no excuse whatever.

'You think she's wrong?'

'I think she's making herself ill and worse than ill over a fantasy,' he said brutally.

Jessica found that her sympathy for the woman spoken about in that dismissive tone overwhelmed the faint dislike she had been entertaining for Sandra.

'Have you told her so?' she asked coldly.

'Oh yes, many times, but she takes no notice.' He shrugged. 'It's her life. If she wants to mess it up, it's nothing to do with me.'

Presumably Chuck Haverford would have said the same thing.

He added acutely, 'And you don't approve of that either.'

Jessica half turned away. 'It's none of my business.'

'No,' he agreed. 'But. . .'

She interrupted him. 'Look, I'm very tired. I've had a wonderful evening, but I've got to get up tomorrow. Shouldn't we be going?'

Leandro was thoughtful. 'Midnight struck, did it, Cinderella? All right, I'll take you home. On one condition.'

'Yes?' she said cautiously.

'That you don't crawl back under your stone and stay there. I shall want to see you. Tomorrow and the day after and the day after that. And if you try and hide from me, I shall come and dig you out.' He grinned at her. 'There's no point, after all. You've told me all your dismal secrets now, haven't you?'

'Yes,' agreed Jessica, aware of a little flare of panic, not at the extent of her revelation so much as at the realisation that he knew exactly how much she had given him in those last, reluctant confidences.

'And no more nonsense about me being a drone and you being a worker. Enjoy the difference.' He pinched her chin impudently.

He was irresistible. Jessica could not help laughing.

'You want to change my character completely,' she complained.

'No, I don't. I love your character—among other things,' he teased. 'I just want you to be a little less tidy sometimes.'

Jessica gave a snort of real amusement. 'Tidy! You should hear my secretary on the subject. She says I can't work unless I've built myself a nest of paper first. And it's true.' She sighed suddenly. 'Except that your uncle's wonderful staff seem to think they ought to clear up after me.'

'Tell them not to,' said Leandro, beckoning a waiter. 'The bill, please.'

'I did. Enrico said he would leave it, but twice I've come back and found everything stacked up neatly.' She sounded despondent.

'Have you?' He sounded alert. 'What did Enrico say?'

'He couldn't account for it. He was very sorry. He offered,' she added with a chuckle, 'to untidy it for me again.'

Leandro laughed. But in spite of the amusement, she had the impression that he had withdrawn from her and that a formidable brain was working behind the absent pleasantries he offered her as he paid the bill and led her back to the boat.

When she was seated again in the speedboat, with the uniformed sailor at the helm, Leandro stood looking down at her for a moment, his hands in his pockets.

'Jessica, I want you to do something for me,' he said abruptly, all laughter banished.

'Yes?' she asked with all her former wariness.

'I want you to lock your door. Both your doors. And if anything frightens you—anything at all, no matter how silly—I want you to come to me at once. Do you promise?'

She did not understand his urgency, but she caught some of it herself. She shivered. Something was wrong, something much more than the vestigial passing attraction Leandro felt for his uncle's architect.

But she was not going to ask him about it. She found she did not want to know.

She said, 'I promise.'

'Thank God for that, at least,' said Leandro harshly and, flinging himself down on the seat beside her, he began to kiss her with force.

CHAPTER EIGHT

THE party was still clearly going strong when they climbed aboard the yacht. There were lights on all the decks and music came from the main cabin. Jessica hung back a little, not wanting to join the throng. She felt shaken and her lips stung—from the salt, she assured herself, not from the almost frantic pressure of his kisses.

'It seems we still have the chance to dance,' remarked Leandro, apparently unmoved by their embraces. His voice was light, amused and just as she would always recognise it.

'It's past my dancing hour,' she told him as coolly as she could. 'I need my rest. You go and enjoy yourself, though.'

He laughed. '*Carissima,* you sound like the old nanny Giorgio once employed for me! She was English too, and she always sounded as if enjoying yourself was dangerous to the health.'

She shrugged. 'It's your health.'

'And my enjoyment. And I'd rather stay with you than go and dance in an overheated saloon,' he told her calmly. 'Your place or mine?'

Jessica began to feel slightly alarmed. As always, she could not make out what he intended to do, if indeed he intended anything beyond throwing her into a flap. He was not only unpredictable, he was capricious, she thought, angry with herself and him.

'I,' she said, 'am going to *my* cabin. Alone.'

'No, you're not,' he contradicted. 'I'm coming too. I want to see if Enrico has done any more of his devastating tidying up.'

She shrugged, not answering. It was not a loverlike reason and he made no attempt, now they were back on the yacht and in the full glare of electric light, to touch her. Though presumably the unfortunate Gianni could not have been under any illusion that he had piloted back to the yacht a lady who had spent most of the voyage locked unresisting in the arms of Leandro Volpi and being ruthlessly kissed. So Leandro's discretion was selective.

Her colour faintly higher than normal, Jessica led the way to her cabin.

Her companion, however, was quite unembarrassed. 'It's about time they decorated this deck,' he observed chattily, drawing flaking paint from the walls on the tip of his forefinger.

Her cabin was not locked, which he noted with a slight frown, and was in darkness. Leandro preceded her inside and flicked on the switch. Then he went through the sitting-room into her bedroom, and she heard him open the door and switch on the light in the shower-room. It was almost as if he was looking for someone, she thought, chilled.

When he emerged, however, he was still very much at his ease.

'I like your nightwear,' he told her, amused. 'Very Cinderella.'

Jessica, to her fury, blushed. Sometimes the maid came in to turn down the sheets and lay out Jessica's cotton print nightdress. She must have done so this evening. Presumably Leandro's ladies did not entertain him in brief cotton shifts printed with bluebells. It was cool and comfortable, but it was not seductive. She glared at him.

'Cinderella, as I recall, wore rags. Are you being rude about my wardrobe, Leandro?'

He grinned. 'I wouldn't dare! I thought it looked very pretty, that's all.' He looked round the cabin. 'As does this room. Is it tidier than you left it?'

Jessica jumped. She had forgotten the excuse he had made for accompanying her to her room. Or maybe it was not an excuse, after all.

'No. We finished this afternoon,' she explained. 'We took the copies to Sandra and then Sue tidied up in here.'

'So where is your copy of the blueprint?' he asked, idly turning over papers and books on her desk.

'In the safe.' She nodded towards a rather fine watercolour of a Tuscan church on the wall. 'Where it will stay until your uncle tells me to get it out.'

'Oh, still all secret, then?'

'It's at the stage where it could be pirated,' she admitted. 'Secret is probably the wrong word. Confidential, maybe.'

'Worth something on the open market?' he queried lightly.

Jessica considered the possibility. 'Not really. Not unless there was some rival concern with an identical site. . .'

'Or the same site?' Leandro asked softly.

Jessica threw him a startled glance. 'But surely that's impossible. I understood Prince Giorgio had bought the land.'

'Some of the land,' Leandro corrected her. 'Bought but not paid for. Or not paid for in full.' He was thoughtful. 'I can imagine a rival being very interested in your ideas, lovely Jessica.' He gave her his most dazzling smile. 'I should guard them with your life, ' he advised thrillingly.

He won a reluctant smile from her, but she was worried. 'Do you really think they're at risk? I haven't been particularly careful about security.'

'I noticed,' he said with a nod at the door. 'Keep it locked from now on, will you, darling?'

'To protect the plans?' queried Jessica, still not quite sure whether the threat was real or not.

He strolled up to her, loose-limbed and graceful, and put a hand on either side of her face.

'To protect you from ravening wolves,' he murmured against her mouth.

It was terrible, she thought in despair, the way her mouth now knew his, responded to his as if they had been kissing each other all their lives. She pushed him away and smoothed her hair, trying to disguise her disturbance.

'What do you think you're doing?'

'Kissing you goodnight,' he said with a lurking smile.

She gave him a dry look.

'Well, you've already told me in no uncertain terms that I'm not welcome to spend the night,' he reminded her. He was clearly enjoying himself. 'So unless you've changed your mind. . . No? Ah, well then, goodnight it has to be.'

Jessica evaded him by the not very subtle expedient of retreating behind a sofa.

'Goodnight,' she said with emphasis. 'I'll lock the door.'

'The best thing in the circumstances,' he agreed with a chuckle, then went to the door and blew her a kiss before slipping quietly out.

Jessica turned the key in the lock behind him with unnecessary force.

He was impossible; he was deliberately provocative; he annoyed her so much that she lost all sense of judgment. She could never tell when he was serious or when he was teasing her mercilessly. She was just too easy a target. Damn him!

She went and showered in an angry mood. Afterwards, for all her professions of tiredness, she found she could not sleep, so she put on the bedside light and leafed her way absentmindedly through one of the paperbacks with which the cabin was provided.

It was then that she heard the knock on the door. It was firm, not at all secretive. Without a second thought Jessica got up and went to open it; she was almost sure it was Leandro. She schooled her expression to one of indifference, though her heart was beating so hard she could barely breathe.

It was not Leandro. Instead, dressed impeccably in scarlet silk and jewels, his mother stood on the threshold.

'Signora Volpi!' exclaimed Jessica, amazed.

The *Signora* swept past her as if she had been invited in.

'I see you are dressed for bed, Miss Shelburne. Is my son with you?' asked the *Signora* in arctic tones.

Before Jessica could recover from her dumbstruck state, the woman had moved to her bedroom and looked inside.

'I see he is not. I assume you are expecting him.'

Jessica gagged and then said with as much of her habitual calm as she could command, 'I have no idea where Signor Volpi may be and I, for my part, would like to go to sleep, *signora*. I would be grateful if you would go.'

'Sleep?' The older woman was plainly unimpressed. 'That is why you are awake with your light on at,' she consulted her watch, 'two o'clock in the morning? Do you think I am a fool, Miss Shelburne?'

'I have no opinion on the subject,' Jessica said carefully, aware that her temper was beginning rise alarmingly.

'You spent the evening with my son. Do not try to deny it.'

Jessica shrugged. 'Why should I? It's the truth.'

The *Signora* showed her teeth in a horrible parody of a smile.

'Miss Shelburne, I do not know what my son may have told you. I know he can be very persuasive when he wants to be, but you should be aware that he is playing a very dangerous game at the moment. No doubt he thinks it amusing to involve you, but I assure you my brother will not be amused. And if Leandro thinks that he can remain Giorgio's heir and behave like a schoolboy in this fashion, then he is even more heedless than I thought him.'

Jessica was quite stunned. Pulling her robe tighter round her, she sank down on to the arm of one of the luxurious chairs with which her suite was provided.

'I don't think I understand,' she said slowly.

Ida Volpi gave her a pitying look. 'Oh, did you think that he would remain my brother's heir—what is your English phrase?—come hell or high water?'

Jessica blinked. 'I didn't think about it at all.'

Signora Volpi gave a harsh crack of laughter. 'Very pretty, Miss Shelburne. Almost convincing. If I were a man I would be most impressed.'

Jessica stared at her.

'I am a woman, my dear,' the other woman said softly. 'I know your game; I have played it myself.'

Jessica began to wonder for a hair-raising minute if the woman were drunk or—worse—mad. Ida Volpi was looking at her as if she hated her.

At last she said, '*Signora,* I am very sorry, but I do not understand a word you are saying. I think you must have the wrong person.' She stood up. 'And I really am very tired. . .'

The older woman grabbed hold of her, the painted nails like claws against her bare arm. The grip was fierce, and Jessica gasped at the unexpected pain.

'Then let me explain myself, Miss Shelburne,' Ida Volpi gritted in a burning whisper. 'I have spent my life— my whole life, do you hear me?—trying to undo my stupidity in marrying Alfredo Volpi and to give my son a chance to have the things that are his right. My right! Who do you think paid for his education? Alfredo would have sent him to a state school and let him go to work in the docks when he was fourteen. It was Giorgio who saved him, Giorgio who educated him.'

Jessica strove to withdraw her arm, to no avail. The *Signora* hardly seemed to be aware of her grip. In fact, Jessica began to doubt whether she even knew who she was talking to.

'I made a life for myself without Alfredo, so that Leandro need not be ashamed of his parents. And Giorgio helped. And see how he repays him! He quarrels with him all the time, will not accept. . .'

She stopped suddenly and her eyes came back to Jessica, suddenly focusing again and looking alarmingly shrewd as they did so. She released her hold on Jessica's arm and spoke more calmly.

'I know he does not agree with this holiday project of Giorgio's.' She shrugged. 'I do not know why. It does not matter. But he has been seducing you to tell him Giorgio's secrets, and that will get him struck out of Giorgio's will for ever.'

Jessica said soothingly, 'Not a secret has passed between us.'

Ida Volpi's eyes narrowed. 'You are like him,' she said on a hissing breath. 'Like Leo. Everything is a game.' She fell silent and then said in a completely different tone, almost composed, 'He won't marry you, you know.'

Totally disconcerted, Jessica sat down hard on the chair behind her.

'I beg your parton?'

'Marriage. He won't,' said the *Signora* succinctly. 'He likes his freedom. I know my son. And anyway, if Giorgio finds out about this, he won't be worth marrying. He had nothing from his father, you know. And I—' her mouth twisted resentfully '—I am my brother's pensioner and have been so for years. Don't delude yourself about my glamorous son: he has no title and no money to speak of and he wouldn't stay faithful to you for a week.'

Jessica said slowly, 'Do you dislike him so much?'

Ida Volpi flushed. 'I—no, of course I don't dislike him. I only want the best for him. He is my son. I love him.'

'Except when he doesn't do what he's told?' asked Jessica, raising her brows.

Two little spots of colour appeared in the *Signora's* cheeks like the painted rosiness on a Dutch doll that Jessica had had as a child.

She said between her teeth, 'You—are—impertinent!'

Jessica leaned back in her chair, crossing one leg over the other.

'And you are not?' she asked gently.

Ida Volpi stared at her as if she had taken leave of her senses. 'I am your employer's sister,' she said, as if that answered everything.

'You are the sister of a man from whom I have undertaken an assignment which is one of many. And which I might choose to resign from,' said Jessica softly. 'I'm a professional, Signora Volpi. I would not take what has just been said to me from Prince Giorgio; I certainly will not take it from you. You have until noon to decide whether you will apologise. If you do not, I shall have no alternative but to offer the Prince my resignation. And tell him why I have reached that decision.'

'You would not dare,' said his sister. She did not say it with much conviction.

Jessica shrugged, not bothering to answer. 'Now will you leave my room, or shall I ring for one of the staff to come and take you away?' she asked, still in the same pleasant voice.

Ida Volpi stared at her, unspeaking. Her elegance seemed to have evaporated. Now she just looked like a desperately tired woman, painted unsuccessfully to hide the lines of envy and discontent. The gorgeous red dress looked like a tent, a piece of brave camouflage. Jessica felt touched with pity.

'I'm sorry,' she said more gently, 'but you should not have spoken like that about Leandro.'

'You are in love with him,' said the *Signora* at last in a rusty voice. She went to the door mechanically, like a puppet manipulated by an inexpert hand. 'You are a fool,' she said without emotion, not looking at Jessica.

She went out, head bent, closing the door softly behind her.

In the uncanny silence that followed her departure, Jessica found that her hands were shaking. She noticed it with faint surprise, watching the hands clasped together on her knee and recognising the faint, uncontrollable tremor as a sign of tension.

When she stood up, however, she realised it was not just her hands. Her whole body was shaking. She felt very cold too. She dragged the robe across her breast, as if it would warm her. She felt sweat on her brow and thought, good heavens, it feels like 'flu!

Then common sense took hold. It had been a nasty little scene, perhaps one of the nastiest in her life. It was not surprising that it had upset her or that her distress had manifested itself physically.

What you need, she told herself, is a stiff drink.

For the first time in her stay on the yacht—for the first time in her life, indeed—she went across to the tray of drinks and uncorked the brandy, splashing some into a glass as the clock struck half past two. She drained the brandy in one swallow and began to feel better. She disliked the taste and never drank it for preference, but now she was grateful for the warmth. The residual nausea of which she had been aware began to subside.

She went across to the door into the corridor and locked it with a vicious movement.

'No more visitors tonight,' she said aloud. 'Not for all the tea in China.'

She took some more brandy and went back to bed, huddling under the bedclothes as if it was winter, instead of a sultry summer night. She lay down, on her side, curling her knees up like a child. The smell of the undrunk brandy in the glass beside the bed wafted over her. She knew she ought to finish it, but she was too cold to uncurl, too tired to lift her head; too frightened by what Ida Volpi had said to want to think about it.

But that's stupid, she thought to herself, circling into sleep. She can't frighten me; I have much more reason to frighten her. If I tell Prince Giorgio. . . If I tell Leandro. . . Though I can't tell Leandro anything or she'll tell him I'm in love with him. She'll tell everyone I'm in love with him.

She did not even know she was crying until the tears dripped into her ears and she had to scrabble them away with the edge of her pillow. In the end she fell asleep with her tears undried. She knew she must have done because the stains were clearly visible in the morning.

Jessica did not usually dream. Normally she fell asleep the moment her head touched the pillow and stayed in that happy state until seven o'clock. But that night she tossed and turned on the edge of wakefulness until late into the morning, a prey to a hundred flickering and rather frightening images. There was a roaring sea that threatened to engulf her. There was a burning sun that bore down on her until she could feel its heat on her face. And in her ear all the time was Signora Volpi's parting taunt, 'You are a fool. You are a fool!'

Eventually she was roused by a scream from the telephone. She struggled up on to one elbow, pushing hair from her eyes, and reached for the instrument.

'Yes?'

'Jessica? Are you all right?' It was Sue, sounding breathless.

'Yes, of course,' said Jessica, coming fully awake. She looked at her watch and her heart sank. Ten o'clock. 'I just overslept, that's all.'

'I was worried. Your door was locked and Enrico said he hadn't been able to get any answer when he brought your breakfast round.'

'I must have been asleep.' She was annoyed with herself and her voice sounded sharp.

'Er—Jessica?' Sue was tentative now.

'Hello?'

'Are you—er—alone?'

'What?' Jessica sat bolt upright so that the mangled bedclothes slid finally and irretrievably to the floor.

'I wondered,' Sue explained, sounding unhappy.

'Yes, I am alone and have been so all night,' snapped Jessica. 'You ought to know me well enough not to have to ask that sort of question, Sue.'

'I'm sorry.' But she sounded happier. 'Can I come along now, then? If I bring your breakfast?'

Jessica snorted but said, 'All right. Give me five minutes to shower.'

Sue actually gave her more like half an hour. When she arrived, the door to Jessica's cabin had been unlocked and Jessica herself was sitting in the window-seat under the porthole, flipping through some drawings. She looked up as Sue came in.

'Good morning. How are you? I should have asked when you rang. Survived the party?'

Sue sank down into an easy chair with a deep sigh.

'Diabolical,' she said.

Jessica was startled. 'What's wrong?'

'Everything,' said Sue comprehensively. She looked very near tears.

Jessica frowned. 'Hangover? Or worse?'

'Hangover *and* worse,' Sue told her frankly. She looked round the cabin. 'Is there any coffee?'

'Not yet. I thought you were bringing my breakfast with you. I'll ring for some.'

'No, I've already talked to Enrico. It should be here any moment.'

As she spoke there came a soft knock on the door and the steward appeared with a tray on which stood three gleaming silver pots, an assortment of delicate china and a basket of sweet rolls. Sue jumped up to clear a space on the low table in front of her chair. Enrico thanked her, depositing his burden.

'I am sorry I have been so long, *signorina,*' he said formally to Jessica. 'There have been one or two problems this morning.'

'I'm not surprised, given the size of the party you had to clear up after,' she told him with sympathy. 'What time did it finish?'

He did not smile, which was unexpected. Normally Enrico was the friendliest of men.

'It is not entirely the party, *signorina.* And it went on until four o'clock. One or two of the guests have stayed the night, I understand.'

He bowed and went out. Jessica looked after him in bewilderment.

'What was all that about? Is Enrico annoyed because I slept late or something?'

Sue shook her head. 'I should think the poor man is going round in circles. All hell has broken loose this morning. You have no idea!'

'Clearly not.' Jessica could not imagine what eventuality would upset the professionally smooth running of the yacht to the extent that Sue suggested. She looked at her secretary with narrowed eyes as she began to pour coffee. Sue was very pale and without make-up her freckles showed clearly. She looked tired too. Perhaps her sense of proportion had diminished in inverse ratio with her hangover.

Jessica added milk to her coffee and passed it across to Sue with the sugar bowl.

'Did you dance until four as well?' she asked gently.

Sue accepted the coffee and groaned. 'I did indeed. I wish to God I hadn't. Everything you ever said about the corrupting influence of the rich and idle I now believe. My head feels as if there's a steam-hammer inside it!'

Jessica found that Enrico had sent her a pot of her favourite hot chocolate. She poured it slowly into the gold-bordered cup.

'Maybe it's accumulated hangovers that are giving poor Enrico hell.'

Sue drank her coffee down in one draught. 'No,' she said. 'No, it's that damned inefficient, stupid, neurotic secretary.'

Sue was normally a moderate girl. She took crises even-temperedly and, even when thoroughly put about by others' inefficiencies, was seldom heard to complain or apportion blame. She said she liked the challenge. At this uncharacteristic outburst, therefore, Jessica stared.

'More coffee,' she said hurriedly, pouring it. 'What's wrong, Sue?'

Sue's tired eyes met her own. 'She's *lost* the presentation. The whole thing. All seven copies of it,' she said in a despairing voice. 'Lost them!'

Jessica sat down heavily on her window seat. She felt stunned.

'But—but how?' she asked at last.

Sue shook her head. 'Don't ask me—I can't even begin to imagine. How *can* you lose two shelves full of heavy files? Unless she heaved the lot into the sea while she was sleepwalking,' she added waspishly. 'God knows she seems to be in a dream most of the time.'

'What does she say happened?' asked Jessica, numb.

'She doesn't. She cries, and shouts a lot. I think the woman's bats,' said Sue in disgust. 'First of all she tried to pretend that we hadn't given them to her, but fortunately Enrico giving us a hand with delivering them meant that I had a witness. So then she said it wasn't meant to be and it was a judgment.'

'A judgment? On whom?' queried Jessica, by now quite bewildered.

For the first time Sue began to look more of her usual lively self.

'Well, I'm not at all sure about that. That was the point at which they started to shut her up and hustle me out of the room. But I think she meant it was a judgment on Prince Giorgio.'

Jessica shook her head. 'I don't understand,' she said helplessly. 'I thought she was a hundred per cent on his side, right or wrong.'

'Mmm, so did I.' For a moment Sue looked amused. 'I rather gathered there'd been a bit more than boss and secretary goodwill between them, in the past at any rate, though no one would think that today. She looked as if she hated him.'

'Maybe she does,' said Jessica indifferently. 'But does she hate me too? What about all my work?'

She frowned. What on earth could have happened? The secretary was a strange, neurotic woman, but Jessica did not think that she was as inefficient as Sue did. She had a cold feeling that something sinister was afoot.

She looked at Sue, who was frowning impatiently. She was clearly annoyed but she did not seem suspicious. Jessica gave herself a little shake. She was becoming foolish, seeing conspirators everywhere. It was a holiday complex development, for heaven's sake, not a nuclear plant.

Yet why had Leandro invited the local Mayor to the yacht in his uncle's absence? Surely he had not been playing politics? Could he have been trying to undermine his uncle's plans? His standing with the community? Yet he had said nothing that could sound like that at the time and nor had the Mayor. Jessica did not think that Simone Spinoletti would prove the most discreet of conspirators, either.

She pushed a distracted hand through her hair, recalling the sharp exchange of words between Sandra and Leandro when Spinoletti came to dinner. Certainly Sandra had defended Prince Giorgio—and seemed to think that he needed defending against his nephew. She stood up, in some agitation.

'They're searching the strong room now,' Sue told her, 'in the faint hope that Sandra might have put them somewhere else.' She grimaced. 'I thought I'd better keep out of the way before I hit someone.'

Jessica gave a faint smile. 'Sounds sensible.' She looked down at her chocolate. 'What on earth do we do now?' she queried musingly. 'I thought I was going to talk to Prince Giorgio this morning, but presumably that's out of the question now.'

'I'd leave it,' agreed Sue. 'Why don't you go shopping or something? Hop into Portofino, buy some lace, go for a walk. Get out of this floating madhouse, anyway.'

'Yes,' said Jessica with sudden decision. 'Yes, let's do that.' She hesitated, looking at the telephone. 'I suppose I just might. . .'

'Leandro,' said Sue with some deliberation, 'is already ashore. Apparently he went with the dawn this morning and said he was going to Genoa. His car keys are gone anyway, or so Enrico tells me.'

'I—see.'

Jessica did her best not to feel let down. From Sue's expression it seemed that she was not doing very well.

'Sightseeing the great healer,' Sue said gently. 'Come along. I'll buy you one of those outrageous ice-creams with cherries and strawberries and half a litre of alcohol.'

Jessica gave herself a little shake and managed a lop-sided grin at her secretary. 'Oh, well, in that case. . .' she said.

CHAPTER NINE

IT was almost a good morning. The sun was brilliant and the little town was, as Sue said, like something out of a fairy tale. Jessica looked out for the painted windows and pointed them out to Sue whenever she detected a false shutter, or balcony. Sue was amused and very impressed. Jessica did not tell her that it was Leandro who had shown her what to look for.

In fact, they did not mention Leandro at all. Sue seemed to have dropped her teasing approval of Jessica's supposed conquest. Indeed, they both steered the conversation away from anything approaching the personal.

Sue bought some lace for her mother. Jessica looked at a designer suit in one of the very smart boutiques off the cobbled port and debated with Sue, over one of the promised ice-creams, whether its cut and admittedly charming colour were worth the price.

The café they chose was overlooking the harbour and they saw various vessels from fishing boats to smart launches arrive and moor and depart. It was a busy scene, but casual. For all its carefree air, however, the port was full of some of the most smartly dressed people that Jessica had seen in years.

'Even their headscarves are designer prints,' said Sue gloomily, watching a tanned blonde go past wearing brief white shorts with the emblem of a famous fashion house on the back pocket. 'I feel outclassed.'

'Don't worry about it,' advised Jessica. 'These people make being beautiful their life work.'

Sue glanced at her quickly. Between them, unspoken, was the name of Leandro Volpi. Both of them looked away and the moment passed.

Yes, it was almost a good morning.

When the time came to return to the yacht, it was with the greatest reluctance that Jessica went to where they had agreed to meet the launch. She felt exhausted, not so much from the shopping and sunshine as from the emotional impact of the previous night. She certainly did not feel happy about the prospect of meeting Prince Giorgio. Of Leandro she tried hard not to think at all.

Of course it was hopeless; he had intruded too much upon her life. As, she remembered with a twist of the lips, he had always intended to do. He had even told her so. What he had not told her was why.

Last night——Well, last night he had made her feel as if there really was a strong attraction running between them, something exceptional. She had felt as if she could trust him, too. Unlike Chuck, he gave the impression that he knew what he was doing, that he knew exactly how important the hypothetical relationship would be to her. And she had felt that it would be equally important to him.

Yet his mother thought otherwise. Sitting silently while Sue chatted to Gianni in fractured Italian, Jessica examined her feelings about that interview with Ida Volpi. She did not like the woman. She hardly knew her, but she had no reason to mistrust her. Presumably she knew her son very well. And she had nothing to gain by coming between Jessica and Leandro, if Leandro was serious.

But for a Riviera heartbreaker, how serious was serious? Jessica stared out across the flat calm of the bay, not seeing its beauties. They were so different. It was all very well for him to tell her to enjoy the differences between them, but he did not take her hesitation seriously. And she—she could not begin to guess what he would take seriously.

She went over in her mind everything they had said to each other from their first meeting. They had sparked at once, crossing swords over his pleasure-loving idleness, her puritanical devotion to work. Their battles had been fun. Jessica acknowledged that.

But last night it had been something more than a battle. And he had not tried to seduce her—or not tried very seriously. Was that because he realised, and accepted, that it was too soon for her, that it would make her feel uncomfortable with herself and him? Or was it rather because he really did not care very much one way or the other?

She could not tell. She had no way of telling. She knew nobody like him, by whom she could judge him. She had known Chuck, of course, who came from the same sort of privileged, luxurious background. But Chuck had been intensely ambitious. She had always known that, even when they were first attracted. Leandro was not intensely anything. Except perhaps laid back, she thought with a reminiscent smile curling her lips. Oh, God, he was so charming. She could love him so much.

She stopped her thoughts right there. She *could* love him. It would be stupid to deny it, at least to herself. But she did not love him yet. She retained enough of her natural caution to keep hold of her heart for the time being, Jessica told herself. He was gorgeous, but she did not know him well enough to commit herself irretrievably, particularly not after her experience with Chuck.

She dismissed the thought that maybe this was not a situation over which she had the control to decide whether she was committed or not. Instead, she held on hard to the reflection that they were still virtual strangers. Leandro knew a great deal about her—he had set out to do so—but she still knew very little about him. And still, at the back of her mind, was the faint, uneasy feeling that there was something she did not understand in his professed attraction to herself, something, as she had once told Sue, with a purpose. She did not see what that purpose could possibly be, but nevertheless the suspicion remained.

Prince Giorgio was too busy to see her when they returned to the yacht. He sent a charming message, hoping she would not be inconvenienced and suggesting that she did everything she could to enjoy herself. The facilities of the boat were at her disposal; she was to take the speedboat if it would amuse her. Or she and Miss York were welcome to play table tennis or billiards. There was a lunchtime barbecue for several guests on the foredeck which he hoped they would attend although, regrettably, he would not be able to be present himself.

All of this Enrico delivered deadpan. Jessica thought about it.

'Why are you telling me this instead of Sandra?' she asked at last. 'Surely it's the sort of message you expect to get from a secretary.'

His eyes flickered. 'I—believe Prince Giorgio's secretary has left the yacht, *signorina*.'

'I see.' She hesitated. 'And Prince Giorgio too?'

'So I am informed.'

'We didn't see him come ashore in Portofino,' she remarked idly.

Enrico inclined his head and murmured something about helicopters. Jessica was surprised. The yacht was large, but she had not thought it was of a size to carry a helicopter launch pad. However, Enrico was clearly determined to say no more, so she did not press him.

Instead, as instructed, she went to the barbecue.

It had clearly been in full swing for some time. She was met by the smell of grilling steaks even before she rounded the corner and saw a white-hatted chef turning meat over on a substantial waist-high barbecue table. There were maybe thirty people there, including Sue and, to her surprise, Simone Spinoletti. Signora Volpi was nowhere to be seen. Nor was Leandro.

One of the waiters whom she recognised greeted her and gave her a plate.

'There is salad, *signorina*. And king prawns. And salmon in aspic which the *Signor* likes.'

She thanked him and helped herself from the generously loaded table. It was too hot for large amounts of red meat she thought wryly, sitting next to a couple who were vaguely familiar. They proved to be guests from a previous cocktail party which she had reluctantly attended during her stay on the yacht, and were interested in the progress of her project.

'I hear Giorgio's very pleased,' said the man, who was perhaps sixty, dressed in flannels and blazer, and holding a plateful of steak and freshly baked bread. 'He was singing your praises.'

'I hear there's a hitch,' said his wife. She was slender and casually elegant, hung about with thin gold chains that must, thought Jessica ruefully, be worth a king's ransom. She looked at Jessica curiously but quite kindly. 'Is that why he's not here?'

Jessica, truthfully, denied all knowledge.

'Nor Leandro,' added her husband.

The woman made a face. 'Oh, darling, you know what Leo's like. He's probably off on one of his crazy schemes, building a bridge somewhere.'

Jessica raised her eyebrows at this unlikely speculation.

The husband laughed, though, and agreed. 'But I thought he was out of commission for a while after. . .'

Before he could finish his sentence, however, the object of the discussion had appeared on deck. Jessica was startled at how glad she was to see him, how she was immediately aware of his presence before anyone else. And it seemed he felt something similiar. His eyes scanned the crowd and seemed to discover her at once. He strolled over.

He was wearing jeans but otherwise, at least by his standards, his dress was formal. He had on a crisp white shirt, the sleeves rolled up to show muscular forearms, the deep collar open at the neck. Over his shoulder a dark jacket was thrown negligently.

The husband remarked on his dress at once. 'You're a bit over-dressed aren't you, Leo?'

Leandro grinned. 'I've been to town. Decency prevailed.'

He kissed the woman's cheek and she gave him her hand.

'Darling,' she said. 'You always look so handsome, even when you're decent.'

Leandro chuckled. 'I wish everyone agreed with you.' He turned to Jessica and put his arm round her with a casual air of ownership that set her hackles up and raised their companions' eyebrows.

'I,' she said captiously, 'have never denied that you look handsome.'

'But. . .' he murmured, laughing down at her; and before she could answer kissed her full on the mouth.

It was a real kiss, not just a conventional brush of the lips in greeting, such as she expected. It was brief, but it was warm and wickedly intimate. His laughing eyes, not hidden for once by dark glasses, defied her to protest. Much to her chagrin, Jessica swallowed and found that she did not have the resolution to protest. He let her go.

'I'm starving,' he announced. He sounded very pleased with himself. 'I've been to Genoa and back and all I had for breakfast was flat orange juice. I need sustenance.'

The woman laughed. 'It looks like it, darling.' She tapped his wrist. 'All those wonderful muscles wilting.'

'They will if I don't get outside a substantial steak,' he agreed, not at all embarrassed by the intimate gesture, Jessica noticed. He flicked a hand at a passing steward. 'Food,' he said. 'Drink. Lots of them.'

The man grinned. *'Si, signor.'*

Leandro sat down on a slatted bench and stretched his long legs out in front of him. Quite as if he were entitled to—as if he knew it would be welcome—he took Jessica's hand and held it lightly.

'What were you doing in Genoa?' asked the man, with a quick look at his wife in which amusement and surprise seemed to be compounded equally.

Jessica was glad he had asked. She did not like to ask herself; it sounded too possessive. She did not want to give anyone, least of all Leandro, the idea that she wanted to be possessive of him. She met his lazy grin with some indignation.

'Clearing something up,' he said cheerfully in answer. 'Eventually.'

'Satisfactorily?' asked the blonde.

'Very much so. A distinct triumph.'

'Another conquest, darling?' the blonde asked, with a faintly barbed look at Jessica. 'Another broken heart?'

He frowned but said pleasantly enough, 'I don't regard broken hearts as an achievement, Sara. And even if I did, I don't think I am so lethal.'

'You wouldn't, darling. You see everything from a man's point of view. Jessica and I know you're lethal,' Sara told him.

'Don't be foolish,' said Leandro, annoyed.

'It's hardly foolish.' The blonde seemed to be in a provocative mood which Jessica recognised was caused, at least in part, by the fact that she was attracted to Leandro herself. 'Remember. . .'

There followed a teasing list of conquests by Leandro and imputed to Leandro which plainly made him furious. Her husband tried and failed to stop the flow. Maybe Sara had had too much sun and wine, or maybe she was feeling reckless in the face of Leandro's indifference. Anyway, she produced a catalogue that, if Jessica had not been wary already, would have worried her extremely.

'Oh, come on, Leo, admit it,' she ended. 'You're an expert on women, from frightened virgins onwards.'

Her husband intervened in a last praiseworthy attempt to deflect the conversation. 'Frightened virgins are a myth, Sara. At least, *I've* never met one. What do you think, Leo?'

'A myth?' Leandro was thoughtful. Whatever he thought about Sara's comprehensive anatomising of his past life, no anger showed in his face, thought Jessica, admiring his control. She knew in her bones that he was angrier than she had ever known him before. 'A myth? No, I don't think so. But I don't think they present quite the difficulty that Sara thinks.'

'Why?' asked her husband.

Leandro shrugged. 'Well, they don't know what they're afraid of. You can talk them out of it, or so I'm told. I've never done it myself.' He gave Sara a cold smile which made her flush and look away. 'No, the real problem is with the frightened lady who is not a virgin and therefore knows exactly what there is to be afraid of.'

Jessica went rigid and withdrew her hand. She managed not to look at him and she managed not to blush, but it was a struggle. She was indignant that he should try to tease her in this cruel fashion in front of other people, but when she looked at him, she saw the seriousness behind the social manner and realised he was not teasing at all.

She stared at him, wondering. He held her eyes very steadily. His smile was lopsided, rueful, but he was definitely not teasing. As if in a dream she put her hand out again. Something flashed in his eyes, quickly veiled, and he covered her fingers with his own.

Sara's husband was talking, still lightly, in that amused, sophisticated fashion. '. . . gone over to the opposition,' he said.

Leandro squeezed Jessica's hand, unseen by the others.

'I don't think I regard a relationship of this kind as quite the battle you and Sara seem to believe it is.'

Sara gave a little scream of laughter. 'Darling, you sound like a social worker! Of course it's a battle. Too dreary if it weren't. Where would be the fun?'

Leandro grinned. 'I could think of one or two areas,' he drawled.

His food arrived and with it glasses and a bottle of champagne.

'Ah, good,' he said, pleased. 'Now I can show Jessica how champagne ought to be opened.'

The smile he gave her was full of complicity, of awareness of what they had already shared, unknowable by their companions. This time Jessica did not manage not to blush.

Leandro took a white napkin from the steward and, having stripped the gold foil and restraining wire from the cork, took the bottle firmly in his right hand, draping the napkin about its neck.

'Observe,' he said. 'Hold the cork firmly. It will probably be beginning to move out on its own anway under pressure from the wine. If it is not, then it is wedged very tightly and the pressure will be that much greater when it is eventually released.'

Sara giggled and put her hands over her ears. Jessica scorned to do so, but she winced slightly, watching the threatening cork.

'All that is needed,' instructed Leandro airily, 'is perfect co-ordination of hand and eye. And a strong nerve. The secret is to turn the bottle, not the cork.' He proceeded to do so. 'And when the cork eventually goes—' there was a restrained pop which made Jessica blink '—keep it close to the mouth of the bottle so that the gas escapes in a controlled fashion, without making the wine fizz all over your shoes.'

There was a faint hiss. It died eventually. Leandro then whipped the cork away and poured the liquid very slowly into four tall flutes. Even the pouring was done carefully so that the wine did not froth up in the glass. Sara applauded enthusiastically. Leandro bowed.

'Voilà!'

Jessica accepted her glass from him rather austerely. It was an impressive talent, she conceded, but one which spoke all too clearly of the habits that made up his life. She gave him a sweet smile.

'If you ever get tired of lotus-eating, you should have an excellent career open to you as a wine waiter,' she informed him.

Sara gasped, but Leandro grinned at her, flicking her nose. 'I've had several offers. I might even consider them.' His eyelids drooped wickedly. He leant towards her and whispered for her ears alone, 'If I were saved by the love of a good woman, for instance.'

Jessica could have kicked him. What was the point of convincing herself that she had lots of room to manoeuvre before she need decide whether or not to fall in love with him when he made her blush and tingle with amusement and excitement like this?

'Thank you,' she said repressively.

'Not at all.' His eyes laughed at her before he turned away to give wine to Sara and her husband. 'You can do it next time.'

'Open the champagne?' she asked, challenging him. She knew quite well that was not what he meant. It was part of his private teasing of her.

He nodded. 'Our very next bottle.' He managed one of his ardent looks. 'I look forward to it.'

Jessica plunged her nose into her champagne flute, positive that even the tips of her ears were scarlet. Damn the man! Why did he think it was such fun to behave like this? And why couldn't she stay immune to his teasing? She was hardly a child, after all.

She bore very little part in the conversation that followed. It was clear that Leandro knew the couple fairly well. They spoke of places and people that were unknown to Jessica. It was almost as if Sara was trying to exclude her, trying to demonstrate that she was not one of the crowd. Maybe also she was trying to hint that she, Sara, knew Leandro better than anyone in Jessica's position would ever begin to. Not, thought Jessica wryly, that that needed demonstrating.

She was not, however, convinced by the hints that Sara threw out, very delicately, that she and Leandro were more than friends. She told him so when, Sara having been claimed temporarily by a mutual acquaintance and her husband being at the bar, Leandro turned to her anxiously.

'I don't know why she's behaving like this,' he said under his breath. 'I've known her for years and never laid a hand on her.'

'Maybe that's why,' returned Jessica under her breath.

He gave her a searching look. 'You believe me?'

She said drily, 'Shouldn't I?'

'Yes, but that doesn't usually seem to determine whether you do or not,' Leandro said, equally drily. 'Have you decided to trust me, after all?'

Jessica swallowed. 'I—don't know.'

'Then come with me. Come with me now,' he said urgently. 'Before they get back.'

She was taken aback. 'But won't it look rude?'

Leandro shrugged. 'I don't give a damn. Do you?' he challenged.

She gave an excited little laugh. 'No, I don't suppose I do,' she acknowledged.

'Then come. *Now*.'

He pulled her hand, taking her after him along the deck. She was amused. She felt like a child escaping from school. She wondered what Sara would think when she returned from her conversation. The woman would not be pleased, she knew. She might not have any claim on Leandro, but she would not want to relinquish the chance of a flirtation—certainly not to a foreigner and an unbeautiful one at that.

She considered Leandro under her lashes. She wondered if he had any real idea how attractive he was. She was beginning to suspect that, in spite of his vainglorious teasing, he was actually quite oblivious of his own charm.

But what had he been doing at Genoa? And why would he not talk about it? She brushed the flickering suspicion away. He would tell her when he wanted to. In the meantime, she knew him well enough to believe that it was nothing dishonourable.

Jessica squared her shoulders and followed him as he swarmed down a rope ladder from the deck.

'Gosh, we are bolting,' she said breathlessly, when her feet touched a wooden floor. 'Where. . .'

He gave a soft laugh. 'Round the bay. As many times as it takes,' he said, and let out the throttle.

It was the speedboat. The floor was not wood after all. Jessica registered it with dismay as he cast off and turned the boat out to sea.

Above the roar of the engine she could hardly think, much less make herself heard. And, as this time they were without the services of a helmsman, Leandro was concentrating all his attention on the boat.

Jessica fell back against the bench seat, a hand at her throat. The boat heaved and pulled like a wild animal. She could feel the powerful engines pounding. The deck beneath her feet shook with them.

'Leandro. . .' She had to shout.

He turned his face towards her, laughing. He was clearly exhilarated by the activity. He was wearing his dark glasses again, but his whole expression was openly one of delight. He shook back his hair as the spray broke over the cockpit shield.

'Wonderful!' he shouted back. 'This is freedom for you!'

If Jessica had been alarmed at their previous journey, this trip terrified her. He seemed to be playing with the boat as if it was indeed a wild animal and one that he was determined to master. The spray drummed against the protective shield with the regularity of gunfire. The boat bucked and rolled. And the distant shore shot past them at a rate that made it feel as if they were on a racetrack rather than at sea.

Jessica closed her eyes. It did not help very much, but at least she did not know exactly how fast they were going if she kept her eyes shut.

It brought back all the worst nightmares: the sound of the engines, the sensation of speed, the smell of petrol. And her own frozen terror, unable to move, unable to protest.

She gave a little moan which Leandro did not hear. In a moment she would be sick with fear. She could not bear it, and yet she was too afraid to touch him, to distract him from his struggle with this demon vessel, in case she surprised him into a mistake and they ended up drowning or, worse, run over by the monster. She began to gabble lines of half-forgotten poetry in her head in a vain attempt to calm her senses.

At last it was over. At last the boat slowed and he cut the engine first to a purr, then to nothing. In the sudden silence the boat rocked as gently as a cradle. Leandro turned to her.

'My darling. . .' He broke off. 'What is it? Jessica, my love, what on earth is it?'

She could not speak. She could not even move, she was trembling so hard. She simply held out her hands to him.

He took her in his arms in a movement so violent that it sent the boat rocking furiously. His head moved against her tousled hair.

'Tell me,' he commanded.

'I——It's very stupid.' Her voice did not sound like her own. It was a mere thread of sound, shaky like faulty tape.

'It doesn't matter, tell me.'

'I—I'm afraid of speed,' she said simply. She pushed her head hard into his shoulder. 'I always have been. Ever since my father. . .'

He lifted a hand and cradled her head.

'Your father? You told me he was killed in a car accident. Oh, God, are you going to tell me you were in the car?'

She nodded, her voice suspended. His arms tightened convulsively.

He swore long and softly. She pulled herself away from him, knuckling her eyes.

'It doesn't matter. You weren't to know. My mother and I were both in the car, you see. My mother won't drive now. I'm not quite as bad as that, but. . .'

'But you don't like speed,' he finished for her. 'And I have to throw Lamborghinis and speedboats at you like a macho schoolboy!'

His voice was so full of fury that she was moved. She put a hand on his shoulder, touching the hair behind his ear shyly but comfortingly.

'No, you mustn't think like that. I could have told you. And for most people it would have been a great treat.'

'And that's what I assumed, didn't I?' Leandro said bitterly. 'Just like you said. I made no allowance for the differences between us. I kept saying they didn't matter. And look what I've done to you as a result! You're trembling like a leaf, my poor love.'

'Like a coward,' Jessica said more strongly. She shook him a little. 'You're not to blame yourself because I'm an irredeemable coward.'

'I'm a fool,' he said, unheeding. 'A blind, insensitive, arrogant fool.'

'That's no worse than being a blind, over-sensitive, arrogant fool,' Jessica said dispassionately.

She was still shaking, but her voice had gained remarkably in strength. She continued, however, to cling to him. He looked down at her.

'I thought we'd go ashore,' he said hesitantly. 'But if you'd rather go back. . .'

She shook her head.

'Or I could leave you here and come and collect you by road?'

She shook her head again. 'I'll be fine. Let's go and sit on the beach. Just let's take the journey back a bit more slowly, mmm?'

His arms tightened again. 'Half a knot all the way,' he promised. 'And now let's get you on to dry land.'

But she could not stand, her legs were trembling too much. She felt a fool and said so, but when she tried to stand her knees buckled and she reached for the side like an old woman.

Leandro caught her.

'I shall have to carry you,' he said, not without a certain satisfaction, Jessica thought.

He did so. They both got extremely wet.

It was not the beach to which he had brought her before. It was hardly a beach at all, just a few stony yards before a clearing of trees and bushes, cushioned with moss. Jessica took off her shoes and let her toes savour the softness of the warm moss, while she sat with her back against a tree.

Leandro waded out to the speedboat and guided it inshore until it was firmly wedged on the beach. Then he came back to Jessica, stripping off his sodden shirt.

'How are you, my poor darling?' he asked, dropping the shirt beside her and going on one knee, taking her hands between his own. 'Still shaking.'

Looking at the handsome face, drawn in anxiety, and the width of tanned muscular shoulder, Jessica thought it was not so very surprising that she was shaking. She said nothing, though.

Very gently he tucked a strand of chestnut hair behind her ear.

'Your coiffure has come adrift,' he said in a still voice.

She put up a hand and loosened the ribbon at the back of her neck, shaking her hair free. For a moment it seemed almost as if he stopped breathing.

Then, very gently, he reached out and combed his fingers through it, drawing it forward over her shoulders as he did so.

He said in a voice shaken by amusement and something else, 'Do you know what a challenge that damned hairstyle of yours is? I've been wanting to do this since the day I first saw you.'

And he leaned forward and kissed her hard. Jessica tensed, not with rejection. Her head tipped back and her mouth opened and she met the kiss with a fervour of her own. It surprised both of them.

When he let her go, he said dazedly, 'How long have you felt like that, for heaven's sake?'

But she did not answer him, not at least with words. The trembling was worse now. It started deep in the core of her body and radiated out, so that every cell of blood and bone felt alive and humming with what was between them. She pulled his head down almost angrily, as her mouth sought his.

He said, half laughing, 'Jess, Jess, we've got to talk.'

But she would not listen. She clung to him, running her hands over his shoulders and down his spine as if she was not sure he was real, as if she could not believe he was there. Her breathing came in short shallow gasps. To the man holding her it sounded almost as if she was crying and he tried to pull away, concerned. But she tightened her embrace and would not look him in the face.

'Hush,' he said, stroking her face, running his lips tenderly along the line of her eyebrow. 'Hush. It's not a race. Don't tremble so, my poor love. The last thing I want is to hurt you.'

Jessica believed him, but nothing could stop the wild trembling now. She ran her thumb the length of his spine between his shoulder blades and down to the belt of his jeans.

'You're crazy, do you know that?' His voice was muffled in her hair. He was trying to stay friendly, she knew, friendly and amused and in control. She moved under him and his voice got harsher. *'Crazy!'*

They were lying full length on the moss, shaded from the full glare of the sun by the tracery of leaves above them. Her T-shirt had ridden up and she felt the imprint of little pebbles and twigs in the moss against her skin. Nevertheless, she did not resist when Leandro began to pull it over her head.

He moved a little, easing on to one elbow, folding the shirt with unsteady hands to lay it gently beneath her head. Jessica could not look at him, but she followed him with her lips, kissing the bare warm shoulder.

'Jess.' His breathing was not much steadier than her own but, unlike herself, he still seemed capable of making sense. 'Jess, my darling, listen to me. Just for a minute.'

Under her hand his chest was rising and falling. She kissed it slowly, using her lips and tongue until he groaned.

'At least tell me this.' He caught her head, held it still, then made her look at him. 'Do you trust me, Jess?'

And she had no reservations, none.

'Yes. Oh yes,' she said in hardly more than a whisper.

A light came into his eyes she had not seen before. He brought her mouth down to his and the kiss spiralled off into outer space.

Jessica was unbearably moved; she had never dreamed it could be like this. Even with Chuck, with whom she had been utterly unguarded, she had never felt this slow, irresistible ascending desire. Leandro was unhurried, deliberate, and yet the urgency was there all the time, accelerating both of them to an intensity that was almost tangible. She twisted and turned in his hands, made half savage by the unexpected heights he was showing her. And in the end he was savage too.

Jessica heard him call her name on a fierce note, almost as if he were in pain, before he sank, breathing hard, on to her breast.

She found herself very still and at peace. Only her hand, in a sort of reflex action, continued to stroke the smooth skin of his back. She looked up through the leaves to a cloudless sky and felt she was floating there, free and soundless as a bird. She gave a sigh of pure happiness.

Eventually Leandro moved, dropping a light kiss on her breast before he looked at her searchingly.

'All right?'

She gave him a lazy smile. 'What do you think?'

He caught his breath and the golden eyes darkened, but he laughed nevertheless and drew a slow sensuous kiss across her parted lips. 'I think you're a danger to shipping!'

She gave a warm chuckle. 'No. No. Only *fast* shipping.'

Leandro hugged her. 'I shall reconsider my promise to return at half a knot, in that case.'

Jessica stretched dreamily. 'I shall probably have a heart attack.'

'That will make two of us,' said Leandro, his voice dry. He leaned forward and trailed a line of kisses between her breasts. 'God knows what my doctors will say. No excitement, they told me.'

'Doctors?' She was still floating, but that worried her, she tried to sit up, but Leandro refused to allow her to, so she subsided again. 'What doctors?'

'A couple of pinstriped types in Genoa. I'll tell you some other time,' said Leandro, clearly preparing for sleep. He pulled her down so that her hair was spread over his chest, and set his arm firmly about her shoulders. His voice began to slur. 'Not important.'

She did not know how long they slept. It could have been an hour or it could have been just a few minutes. It felt perfect, relaxed against him in the warm shadow, his arm round her protectively.

At last he stirred, running his hand down her body rhythmically as he woke. Already it felt familiar.

He said, 'I suppose we need to go back.'

'I suppose,' she agreed without enthusiasm.

'I more or less hijacked the speedboat. I'd better let Gianni know it's safe.'

'You more or less hijacked me,' Jessica pointed out sniffily. 'Who are you going to assure that I'm safe?'

He gave a chuckle. It rumbled under her ear like underground tremors.

'You're not safe, you're dynamite,' he told her, beginning to sit up.

Jessica followed suit, rubbing her ear. 'That tickled,' she complained.

Leandro was unrepentant. 'You'll just have to get used to it, I guess.'

She dressed slowly, weighing his words. Did he mean she would have to get used to it for the rest of the time she was on the yacht? But he said he did not have brief circumscribed affairs and she believed him. So he must mean get used to it permanently. Could he possibly mean that?

He took the speedboat back to the yacht very slowly. His arm was round her all the way, tightening whenever she showed the slightest sign of flinching. He told her how it worked too, in minute and distracting detail, so they were back almost before she knew it.

They tied up and then, as she turned to climb aboard, he stopped her, turning her back to face him. He looked very grave.

'Jessica.' He scanned her face. 'Do you—regret this?'

She shook her head, without hesitation.

Leandro said, 'Look, I have to see Gianni and I've got to talk to Giorgio as well. But I don't want to let you go.' He held her to him, laughing a little into her hair. 'I'm a fool, I know. Don't tell me. I just don't want to see you walk away from me. Not after this afternoon.'

Jessica took his head between her hands and kissed him gently.

'Then what do you want me to do?' she asked softly.

His arms tightened. 'I want you to go straight to my cabin. Wait for me there. Not talk to anyone else or be with anyone else. Only me.' He held her away from him and looked down into her smiling eyes. 'Is that too much to ask of an independent lady?'

She shook her head, her hair swinging about her shoulders. He took a strand of it and carried it to his lips.

'You're wonderful,' he said. He fished in the pocket of his jeans. 'The key. I won't be long.'

They climbed aboard. On deck nobody was in sight and they clung together, kissing.

'Hey,' protested Jessica, drawing away at last. 'This isn't a last goodbye!'

'It's the end of the beginning, though,' said Leandro, unwontedly sober. Then he gave his unmistakable grin. 'Pity, really. I enjoyed the beginning, in spite of the scars.'

They parted.

Jessica already knew where his cabin was. She went to it slowly, aware of some trepidation. It was like being an invader, this going into someone else's room alone, even on such a pressing invitation. For a moment she pondered going first to her own cabin to shower and change. She rejected the thought. For some reason it was important to Leandro that she went first to his cabin, so she would do it. She owed him that much.

His room was devastatingly tidy after the chaos in which she lived. There were a few books on the table in the middle of his saloon, but apart from that not a thing was out of place, not even the exquisite velvet cushions or the neat arrangement of inkstand and monogrammed blotter on the desk.

Jessica hesitated before going into his bedroom. But that was undoubtedly what he would want, she thought wryly, so she went.

There was almost nothing there either that gave a clue to his personality. A dark blue robe hung behind the door with the di Stefano monogram on it, so presumably it too was an accessory of the yacht. There was a tracksuit, though, flung over an upholstered chair. It looked as if Leandro had left it to be laundered: it was creased and there were great flakes of paint along one of the sleeves.

On the bedside table was a plain alarm clock with a soft leather pouch beside it. Both looked old and stained. Jessica inferred that they were old friends, unlike the bathrobe.

She looked around the room. There was absolutely nothing else, not so much as a half-read book on his bedside table. Though—she looked closer—she thought there was some odd cloth arrangement on the table, too heavy to be a handkerchief. She picked it up and it fell into the folds of a surgical blindfold. She stared at it confused. Did he sleep blindfold? Why? She had heard of light sleepers blocking their ears with earplugs, but surely nobody needed to bandage their eyes while they were asleep?

She heard the outer door go and went back into the saloon, expecting to see Leandro. Instead, to her intense embarrassment, she met Sue York's shamefaced gaze.

'Oh, Jess, you *are* here. I was so afraid. . .'

'Afraid?'

'You don't understand—you've been out of the way. Oh Jess, it's been terrible!'

And, most uncharacteristically, Sue sank on to the velvet chaise-longue under the Sheraton mirror and wept. Jessica crossed to her and put her arm round her shoulders.

'What's happened? Has someone been rude to you? Tried to blame you for what Sandra's done?' she asked, speculating wildly.

She shook her head, sniffed, and drew an already soaked tissue from one sleeve to blow her nose.

'No, worse than that. It's the plans. Your copy of the plans. They've gone!'

'*What?*'

'Gone,' repeated Sue in a stronger voice. 'Prince Giorgio came back and asked if there was another copy and I said yes, of course, and went to the safe and—they weren't there.'

'But that's ridiculous,' said Jessica. 'I put them there myself yesterday—you saw me.'

'I know. And nobody knew they were there except you and me.'

'No.' Suddenly and sickeningly Jessica recalled telling Leandro; more than telling him, had she not actually waved at the picture, virtually showing him where the safe was?'

'What is it?' asked Sue quickly.

'Nothing,' said Jessica unconvincingly. She had gone very white.

Was this why he had not wanted her to go back to her own cabin? To keep her from finding out that the safe had been rifled?

Sue said, 'Do you realise that if it hadn't been for the set you mailed to Andrew, there wouldn't be any record of the plans at all? Or any proof that you'd done the work?'

Jessica shrugged. 'That wouldn't be the end of the world. I dare say I could put them together again. Unless all my workings have been stolen as weil?' she added as an afterthought.

Sue shook her head. 'They're all still there on your desk. At least, as far as I can tell. I checked and I couldn't see that there was anything missing.'

'So why bother to steal all these copies?' asked Jessica, pale but still fighting.

'Because apparently Prince Giorgio has to talk to the local people by the end of this week,' said Sue. 'I didn't know that. Did you?'

Jessica shook her head very slowly. She felt as if her heart had suddenly grown too big for her chest. It hurt.

'He was keeping it quiet because he didn't want a big protest meeting, I think. Sandra knew, but no one else.'

'Spinoletti,' said Jessica in an unrecognisable voice.

'Oh, the Mayor. Yes, well, he had to know, of course. He arranged it.'

'So if he knew, presumably Leandro Volpi also knew,' said Jessica in a voice like iron filings on steel.

Sue's eyes met hers in sympathy.

'Yes, I suppose so.' She did not say that she had already come to the conclusion that Jessica was now painfully and so reluctantly reaching.

Sue said, 'I don't understand, because it's something to do with ecclesiastical law, I think, but if Prince Giorgio can't convince them that his scheme is a good one this week, they can stop him more or less permanently. He needed your plans because they show where and how the water source will be tapped, demonstrating that it won't be deflected from the village or the fields. And now he can't do it.'

'Yes, he can. Unless Andrew's copy has been lost in the post,' said Jessica. 'Have you rung him?'

'Not yet. I wasn't sure what to say.'

'And didn't trust the lines from the yacht?' Jessica gave a wintry smile. 'Very wise. Don't ring him. I'll fly back to London myself and collect them. If I'm too late for a flight this evening, I'll stay overnight in Genoa and pick up the first flight out in the morning.'

Sue said, almost imploringly, 'Jess, you don't *know* it was him.'

'Don't I?' asked Jessica bleakly.

'It could have been anyone. The servants, say.'

'They've been here for years.'

'Well, Signora Volpi, then,' said Sue desperately. 'I wouldn't say she's long on loyalty.'

'Maybe not, but she likes money. I can't imagine her doing anything that would make Prince Giorgio less rich.'

'One of the guests from the party then. Or Sandra, even.'

'Don't be silly, Sue,' Jessica said wearily. 'I know you're trying to help, but it really hasn't got much point.' She swallowed suddenly, remembering something else. 'His tracksuit in there has got paint on it. I remember seeing that the paint was flaking in our corridor. And when I walked into a door—well, I didn't, I was hit over the head.' She shut her eyes tight. 'He must have done it. I wasn't sure at the time, but now. . .'

Sue said gently, 'Go to him. Ask him. Don't condemn him unheard, not if it's important.'

'It isn't important at all,' said Jessica with resolution. 'Not to me. Not to him. Except of course it is nice to know why he's been chasing me as he has. I was beginning to wonder. It's always satisfying to have a mystery solved.' Her voice broke.

Sue looked appalled. 'You're in love with him,' she whispered.

'*I am not!*' It came out like a whiplash.

'Jess, for heaven's sake!'

Jessica almost pushed past her. 'I shall go and see Prince Giorgio,' she said. 'At once. Would you talk to Enrico about getting me off this damned ship and back to Genoa, please?'

She did not wait for Sue's reply. Prince Giorgio's apartments were in a corridor at right angles to Leandro's. She went in after only a perfunctory knock. Leandro and his uncle were confronting each other, looking very stern. Their expressions turned to amazement when she appeared, then Leandro took a step towards her.

She ignored him, addressing herself to his uncle. 'I'm told that my own copy of your plans is missing.'

The Prince looked startled at this abrupt statement. 'Well, yes, but. . .'

'I am to blame,' said Jessica in her most professional voice. 'I should have delivered them to you personally.'

If possible, the Prince looked even more uncomfortable, 'My dear young lady, you are hardly to blame. I cannot involve you in my—er—private affairs, but I can assure you that no blame attaches to you whatever.'

'Nevertheless, I must do what I can to make amends.'

The Prince looked tired. 'My dear child, what can you do? I have been very secretive, but I suppose your excellent secretary has told you that I need a full set of the plans by Friday night. Even if you worked the clock round, you could not reproduce everything in that short time.' He shrugged. 'I must resign myself and chalk it up to experience.'

'That will be unnecessary.' Jessica spoke with precision. She avoided Leandro's eye. 'I posted a copy to my partner, for his views and for our archive. I will have it copied and return it to you.'

They both stared at her.

'But—I did not think it would be possible.' The Prince gave a great shout of delighted laughter. 'But that is wonderful! Do you hear Leandro? It will not be total defeat after all!' He clasped her to him and kissed her enthusiastically on both cheeks. 'I did not know what a treasure I was employing when I gave you the contract, my dear Jessica. I congratulate you. I congratulate myself. Leandro, my boy, you will see, you will see!'

'I look forward to it.' Leandro's voice was even. You would not have thought that he had been totally found out and defeated at every turn. In spite of her misery, Jessica could not help admiring his cool.

'I'll go then,' she said. 'If I could just borrow a ride into Genoa?'

'I will take you,' Leandro said swiftly.

Jessica sucked in her breath. 'No, thank you.'

'But certainly. . .'

'I would rather you did not,' she said in a voice of deadly quietness.

Prince Giorgio, suddenly distracted from his transports of triumph, looked sharply between the two of them.

Leandro said, 'If I promise to leave the Lamborghini behind, will you let me drive you to Genoa?'

Jessica turned to face him then, her green eyes wide and steady.

'I think I would prefer to be certain that I will arrive,' she said clearly. 'Prince Giorgio will send me in one of his chauffeur-driven cars.'

Leandro looked as if she had struck him.

The Prince said, 'Of course, of course. But I assure you, you would be quite safe with Leo.'

Jessica gave a crack of laughter before she could stop herself. Leandro's head went back. His mouth was a grim line and he looked suddenly very tired.

Jessica said to the Prince, 'I do not want to pry into your family affairs, *signor,* but can you tell me that you don't know who stole the plans?'

'No,' he said heavily. 'No, I cannot do that. I know very well, as I think you must also by now.'

'Yes,' agreed Jessica. She felt sick. 'It's obvious, when you know the answer, of course. And I don't want to get involved. So I prefer to take a car driven by a stranger, if you don't mind.'

The Prince cast an apologetic look at Leandro. 'But—forgive me, my dear, I understood that you were already involved in my family.'

'No,' said Jessica in a voice not much above a whisper. 'No. And I don't want to be. I'll just get my case and go.' She let her glance rest somewhere in mid-air between them. 'I'll bid you both goodbye,' she said, before she fled.

Sue had her overnight case packed. There was a shoulder bag with lire and travellers' cheques in a pouch beside it, together with her passport.

'Are you sure you'll be all right?' Sue asked worriedly.

'Yes.' Jessica checked her papers and zipped them into the overnight case's safety pocket.

'There's a late flight; it leaves at ten-fifteen. If you miss it I've booked a hotel room—you'll find the reservation in your passport. Go straight to the Alitalia desk, they'll have your flight tickets. I paid by American Express, so all you need to do is pick them up and board.'

Jessica hugged her. 'Thank you. I'll see you in London. Come back as soon as you've cleared up here.'

'You're not coming back, then?' said Sue, not really surprised.

'Andrew can do it.' Jessica gave a travesty of a smile. 'I've earned a holiday. I'm going to stay with Mother, I think.'

Sue nodded. 'Well, good luck. And bon voyage.'

Jessica went swiftly to the boat deck. A dark figure detached itself from the railings and handed her down the companionway into the launch. She did not look at him, she was so blinded by tears.

There were two others in the launch: Gianni, whom she knew, at the helm, and a short fat man who doubled as steward and chauffeur. Presumably he would be driving her to Genoa.

In her ear Leandro said, 'Unless you change your mind.'

Jessica went rigid. She did not turn, continuing to stare straight ahead at the back of the little man's head.

Leandro said, 'Why are you running away, Jess?' There was no laughter in his voice at all. 'Second thoughts?'

'First thoughts,' she corrected hardily. 'This afternoon I wasn't thinking at all.'

'Oh, my love!' He put out a hand to stroke her hair and she recoiled violently. His hand fell to his side. After a pause he said, 'I won't try to stop you, Jess. But you can't go on running for ever. When you're ready we'll talk.'

'I do not,' gritted Jessica through her teeth and an infuriating film of tears, 'want to talk to you.'

'Not now, perhaps. . .'

'Ever,' she said with unmistakable conviction.

He shook his head—as if she was the one who was at fault, she thought, her temper flaring. He said soothingly, 'Things will look different tomorrow.'

'No, they bloody well won't!' She rounded on him as her temper went up like a flare. 'You've shot your bolt with me, Leandro Volpi. Oh, you were very clever, very convincing. I'd never have guessed it was just for show. But I've found you out now and I don't want any more of it. Do you understand me? I don't ever want to see you again!'

She was panting by the time she had finished. Apart from the steady chug of the launch's engine there was absolute silence. Leandro stood like a statue.

Then he said slowly, 'You said you trusted me.'

Jessica gave a hard crack of laughter. 'Yes. That must have given you a good laugh!'

He turned away sharply. 'Were you lying then?'

'I told you—I wasn't thinking. It will teach me,' she said bitterly, 'to keep my wits about me in the future.'

'It will indeed.' His voice sounded muffled.

They were coming into the little port, curving carefully between the moored sailing vessels. Leandro went to the prow to help the others. Finally they were still and the engine was cut.

Leandro came back to her, helped her courteously to disembark. She found, in the lights of the port, that he was wearing his dark glasses again. Her lip curled.

'Really, you're just one affectation after the other, Leandro,' she said disdainfully, and flicked the glasses off his nose on to the paving stones.

He stood rocklike, not attempting to retaliate, not attempting to pick them up.

'Goodbye, Jessica,' he said in a remote voice. 'I hope you will be happy.'

He turned his back on her and jumped back into the boat before she could find a suitable retort.

CHAPTER TEN

THE journey home passed in a haze. Jessica sat in the aeroplane like a zombie, feeling emotional exhaustion wrapping around her like another life. She looked blankly at the air hostess when she was offered a snack, accepted wine which she forgot to drink, and eventually fell into an unreal torpor that had the appearance but not the relaxing qualities of sleep.

The flight went to Gatwick. The arrival hall was almost empty. They must be the last flight of the day, she thought. That would mean there would be no taxis; she had arrived late at Gatwick before. Oh well, the train was just as quick, though less convenient, and she was too tired to care much about anything.

But Andrew Lamont was waiting for her at the barrier, his childish face screwed up in an expression of respectful gravity, his natural exuberance damped.

'You look all in,' he told her, escorting her out to his waiting car.

Andrew fancied himself as a sportsman and as a result his chosen vehicle was one designed to carry hockey sticks and fencing foils in preference to people. Jessica slotted herself into the passenger seat, swinging her feet sideways to avoid a pair of mud-encrusted hockey boots.

'Sue sounded very mysterious,' said Andrew tentatively, having negotiated his machine on to the motorway. 'Conspiracies galore, I gather.'

'Yes.' Jessica sounded as empty as she felt.

'Um—is there anything I can do?' he asked, rather pink-faced at the embarrassing intimacy of the question.

'Not a thing,' she told him. 'Except take your copy of the plans out to Portofino.'

'That's in hand. I've already had copies made, and I've lodged one at the bank for good measure,' he added, plainly proud of himself for his forethought.

'Good thinking,' Jessica congratulated him. 'I wish I'd had the sense to do that at the start. Not that it will make that much difference now. The Prince knows who stole the blueprint and *he* knows there are other copies. So it's checkmate.'

'Ah.' Andrew drove for several minutes in silence. 'He?' he asked at last, delicately.

'Leandro Volpi,' said Jessica without expression.

'Oh, you mean the nephew chappie.' Andrew whistled silently. 'Gosh! Family feuds in a big way there.' He looked at her curiously. 'He was the one you called the Body Beautiful, wasn't he?'

She swallowed. 'Yes. He is—very.'

'Gosh,' said Andrew again, sounding faintly put out. He was kind and talented and enthusiastic, but he was little and round; nobody was ever going to call him beautiful. 'Sounds a bit of a pain.'

Jessica nodded her head. 'That too.'

'Sounds to me as if you're well out of it,' Andrew told her.

'Yes,' she agreed desolately. 'Yes.'

She saw him off in the morning. To begin with he was not inclined to play messenger boy, but he grew so intrigued with the tales of high living and family feuds that he extracted from Sue's telephone conversation, that in the end he decided to make the immense sacrifice and travel out to Italy himself.

With Sue and Andrew both out of the office, Jessica was tempted to stay in London and remain the public face of Shelburne and Lamont. But she was too tired to concentrate and too wretched to pretend, so in the end she decided to surrender to her feelings.

'I'll be at the address on the index card,' she told Sue's assistant. 'Don't give the phone number to anyone, or the address, but if there's anything you can't handle you can get in touch with me there.'

'What if anyone rings for you?' asked Diane professionally.

'I'm out of town taking a short break and can't be disturbed. I'll call them when I get back in a week or so. In the meantime, they can talk to Mr Lamont who will be back the day after tomorrow.'

'Right,' Diane nodded. She gave Jessica a sunny smile. 'You certainly look as if you could do with a holiday, Miss Shelburne. You must have been working a twenty-hour a day. Have a nice time.'

'Thank you,' said Jessica drily.

Her mother was surprised to see her. She too echoed Diane's strictures.

'Is it work that has done this to you?' she asked after dinner on the first evening.

Jessica's smile slipped a little. 'That's what everyone keeps asking me.'

Her mother asked quietly, 'Are you in trouble, Jessica?'

She bit her lip. 'I don't know. I hope not, but maybe.'

Her mother's brows rose. 'Surely you know?'

'No, not yet. It all depends on whether I can get over it. This time.'

'Ah,' said her mother, putting both elbows on the table and resting her chin on her hands. 'A man.'

Jessica's eyes flashed. 'Is it so surprising?'

'No, dear,' her mother said calmly. 'I've been expecting it.'

'What?'

'The only surprising thing,' she went on, unheeding, 'is that it hasn't come before. One bad apple—Chuck— and then you more or less went into purdah. It's not normal, Jess.'

Jessica gave a spurt of laughter. 'That's just about what *he* said.'

'Then he sounds sensible, at any rate.' Her mother looked at her narrowly. 'Have you known him long?'

'Less than a month,' said Jessica defiantly.

If she hoped to shock her mother she was disappointed. 'They're always the worst, the ones you fall for immediately. I remember I realised I was in love with your father after about ten minutes.'

'I am not,' said Jessica, goaded, 'in love with him.'

'Aren't you, dear? Or do you just not want to be? It doesn't usually work, you know,' said her mother kindly.

Jessica left the table abruptly and retired to bed. Her mother, with what she felt was a total lack of maternal sympathy, could be heard singing blithely as she washed up in her pretty kitchen.

The next day Jessica announced that she was going to work in the garden. Her mother acquiesced. Jessica set about digging up a huge patch of plantains and goose-grass with a will. She refused to stop for lunch, going grimly on with her work until her hands were sore where she gripped the fork and her back was aching.

It was as she was taking another ferocious thrust at a clump of weeds that she heard a step behind her.

'You're going to ache tomorrow if you go about it in that way,' said Leandro's voice in exactly the light, amused tone which had been echoing in her head for the last two days.

Jessica gasped and her sweaty hands lost their grip on the implement. Leandro caught it neatly, and drove it, one-handed, into the earth. Then he came close up to her and tilted her face up for his inspection.

'I don't think hard labour agrees with you,' he said at last. 'You look tired.'

She snatched her chin away, compressing her lips.

'What are you doing here?'

'Chasing you, of course,' he said, as if it was obvious. 'I told you we would need to talk.'

'That wasn't what you said when we said goodbye in Portofino,' Jessica muttered. That goodbye had hurt, for all that she knew she had deserved it and did not really want anything different.

'Ah, but you had hurt my feelings, my darling. I was smarting, and I was very angry.'

'So why have you come here now? To carry on being angry?'

He shook his head. For once he was not wearing those detestable glasses.

'When your excellent Miss York explained, I forgave you at once,' he told her smugly.

Jessica glared at him. 'Forgave me for what?'

'For not trusting me, of course,' said Leandro, and took her into his arms.

She had been wrong. He was not laughing; he was not in the least amused. His mouth seeking hers had the hunger of desperation and his arms were shaking.

At last he raised his head and gave an unsteady laugh.

'And now I suppose you'll have to forgive me for rushing my fences again.'

Jessica disengaged herself slowly. That kiss had shaken her more than she wanted to admit.

She said uncertainly, 'Are you trying to tell me you want me? I mean really want me? Not just for the plans, or anything?' She was incredulous.

He shut his eyes briefly. 'What do you think?'

'I think you're wasting your time,' she told him frankly. 'There's a copy in the bank now, so even if you managed to throw Andrew's in the sea, it will be preserved for posterity.'

He took her by the shoulders and shook her. 'I don't give a damn about your plans, or Andrew's, or the bank's, or my uncle's whole damned project. I told him when he started it that it wasn't my scene and I didn't want anything to do with it, and that still stands. It is none of my business.'

Jessica stared at him. 'Then why did you have Spinoletti to dinner?'

'He's an old friend. He asked me how he should approach my uncle—they were worried about their water supply. My uncle Giorgio is not the sort of man who would bother about someone else's water supply if it inconvenienced him. I gave Sim a bit of advice, that's all. No conspiracy. No threats.'

'Then why did you get involved with—I mean, flirt with me?'

'You mean get involved with,' Leandro assured her grimly. 'And because I couldn't help myself. Heaven knows, it was bad timing. I never meant to.'

Jessica flinched.

'Don't look like that,' he said. 'It's nothing to do with you. It's just that I'd had an accident, and I was supposed to be convalescing. It's not easy,' he added with a grin, 'to woo and win a lady of your suspicious nature and convalesce at the same time.'

'Accident?' So that was why he had spoken of doctors on that day on the beach. Jessica went towards him anxiously. 'What sort of accident?'

He hesitated for a moment, then he shrugged. 'I'd better tell you, I suppose. You'll only find out later and start suspecting me of things if I don't.' He looked round. 'Can't we go inside or something? I feel this might take some time.'

She led the way into the conservatory. Once inside he did not reach for her, as she had half expected, but leaned against a workbench, watching her carefully.

Leandro said slowly, 'You've always thought I was a terrible playboy, haven't you, Jessica?'

'Wasn't that what you wanted me to think?' she retorted.

'No—I—oh, yes, damn it, I suppose it was.' He gave a snort of self-disgust. 'I was so sure I had you summed up, you see. One look round that apartment of yours and I thought, aha, here's a lady who lives entirely for work. It was so tidy, almost ascetic. It hardly looked lived in at all. It was as if all your real energies were poured out in work. Your office looked more like a home than your home did.'

'That's—very fair,' said Jessica, taken aback and faintly shamefaced.

'Oh, yes, that may be fair; the rest of it wasn't.'

'The rest of what?'

'Of my brilliant conclusions,' said Leandro grimly. 'I decided, you see, that you'd taken refuge in your career because you could not handle your own sexuality. I never dreamed there was someone like Chuck—to say nothing of your mother's history—in your background. I just took one look at the obvious and leapt to all the wrong conclusions.'

She said, bewildered, 'Did it matter?'

He looked at her impatiently. 'Of course it mattered. If I'd realised, I wouldn't have been so complacent. I thought all I needed to do was shake you up a little. Make you realise that you were attracted to me, if you like.'

He saw her flinch and his mouth compressed.

'Yes, well, it didn't work out quite like that. I was determined, you see, to make you give in, to make you acknowledge that work was not the most important thing in life. I was pretty certain that you would not find time for me if I approached you in the ordinary way, but if you thought I was a loafer and a playboy, you might just be intrigued. Irritated but intrigued. Otherwise, I didn't think I stood a hope, not from what I had heard, anyway.'

Jessica thought of the escorts who had never managed to achieve more than a quarter of her attention. 'You were probably right,' she mumbled.

'Up to a point. The important thing, though, was that I didn't realise you'd already bumped your nose on the sort of golden youth I was pretending to be and had the scars to prove it.'

She shook her head decisively. 'You're wrong there. Chuck worked a great deal harder than you've ever suggested you might be prepared to do.' She gave a small laugh. 'I don't think your tactics were so wrong, after all.'

'But they hurt you,' he said shrewdly.

Jessica could not answer that. She turned her eyes away and said with an effort, 'You were going to tell me about your accident.'

'It was Sandra, of course. You may have guessed.'

'Sandra? She made you have an accident?'

'She tried to kill herself,' Leandro said soberly. 'Throw herself off a cliff, to be precise. You may remember I nearly scared you out of your wits once when you were leaning over the edge.'

On the hotel terrace the night of the sunset, Jessica remembered.

He said apologetically, 'It brought back too many memories too quickly. I'm not normally an hysteric, but, with Sandra, one moment she was looking at the view from one of the vine terraces, the next she was launching herself into space.'

'She was hurt? You both were? I remember Enrico saying something about her being ill,' murmured Jessica.

'No, she wasn't hurt. I caught her.' Leandro grimaced. 'Not very heroically. I dived at her legs in a sort of rugby tackle and got her just in time. The trouble was, I hit my head quite hard. I was concussed. Then, when I came round, I couldn't see properly. They told me to take three months off and then they would look again to see if I needed surgery.' His mouth was wry. 'Hence the dark glasses you so object to. To say nothing of the lolling around in the sun.'

'Oh, lord,' said Jessica, deeply ashamed and full of foreboding.

'Sandra wasn't hurt in quite the same way. They diagnosed a nervous breakdown. We were fairly sure it had been coming on for some time.' He cleared his throat. 'She had an affair with my uncle, you know. It went on for several years, then he got tired of her.'

Jessica said, 'Was it Sandra who destroyed the plans, then?'

'I am afraid so. She's still a bit crazy, you know. Half the time she loves Giorgio, thinks she is the only person in the world who can protect him from his enemies. The other half,' he shrugged, 'she hates him. I think she threw the plans overboard thinking that the project was desperately important to him and he would be hurt. I know she knocked you out, trying to frighten you away before you finished them.'

'Isn't it important to Giorgio, the project?'

'Not in the way she thought, poor woman.' Leandro passed a hand over his eyes. 'You know, when we found out, she went to pieces. She was shouting and screaming, throwing herself around. I think it shook Giorgio. He wasn't there before, when she tried to jump. Anyway, he had her air-lifted off to hospital by helicopter at once. And I think he's pretty ashamed of himself.'

'That's what he meant when he said he wouldn't involve me in his private affairs,' Jessica said slowly. 'I thought he meant it was you and he knew it.'

'I know you did, my darling. As I said, Miss York explained. I must say it never occurred to me at the time. I just thought you'd decided you didn't want to have any more to do with men who scared you silly and then jumped on you.'

Jessica found that, in spite of the light tone, the golden eyes were very intent. She swallowed deafeningly.

'Oh.'

He said, 'Will you tell me now, my darling? Did I take you too far too fast that afternoon?'

She said in a strangled voice, 'I don't know what you mean.'

'I mean that I never meant to rush you like that. I knew this man, Chuck—' he said the name with distaste '—had hurt you badly and I was full of good intentions to prove to you how much more reliable and sensitive and generally an excellent thing I was. Only I rather got carried away.'

Jessica lifted her chin. 'As I recall,' she said in her professional lady tone, 'we both got carried away.'

'Yes, but you were scared half out of your mind by my stupid game with the boat. You weren't responsible. . .'

'I was perfectly responsible,' said Jessica, ruffled. 'I very much wanted you to make love to me. I'd been wanting you to,' she added for good measure, 'for days.'

Leandro stared at her. The mask had slipped with a vengeance now. He looked bewildered, uncertain. It suddenly occurred to her that he was no less vulnerable than she, and she had hurt him a great deal worse.

She drew a deep breath and said, 'I hope you'll do so again very soon. If you can forgive me, that is.'

There was an unnerving silence while she blushed fierily and Leandro looked as if he had been sandbagged.

At last he said tonelessly, 'Say that again.'

Jessica, whatever her failings, was no coward. She lifted her chin, ignored her hot cheeks, and repeated her observation.

She was taken into a comprehensive embrace.

'Oh, my love, my darling, you wonderful, wonderful girl,' Leandro said, kissing her fiercely. 'Whenever and wherever you say, my love. Just as long as at some point you let me marry you.'

Jessica, who was kissing him with equal frenzy, stopped dead.

'Marry?' she echoed dazedly.

'I'm sorry if you don't care for the idea—' the laugh was back in his voice '—if it offends your independence or anything like that, but I don't want any more mistakes or misunderstandings or messing about. You and I belong together and always have done. So we might just as well get married and make sure the rest of the world takes note.'

Jessica was dazed. 'But what about my job?'

'What about mine?' countered Leandro at once.

She gave him a reproving look. 'I didn't know you had one until today,' she reminded him.

'I told you, I'm a perfectly respectable engineer. I build oil rigs and things. I have to travel a lot. Perhaps you could come with me, sometimes.' He tucked her hair behind her ear. 'When you want me to make love to you,' he added, earning himself a look of burning indignation. He kissed the tip of her nose. 'What do you think?'

'I don't know. I never thought about it. Your family. . . Your mother. . .'

His mouth tightened and he stopped laughing. 'My mother need not concern you,' he said deliberately.

Jessica was shocked and looked it.

He gazed down into her eyes. 'Listen, I hardly knew my father because of her. She resented him for not being rich and worldly like Giorgio, so she left him when I was a child and did her best to turn me into a sort of substitute son for Giorgio. God knows what sort of complex that would have given me if Papa hadn't stuck around. He used to take me off for sneak holidays. She couldn't prevent him, but when he used to come to pick me up she would treat him like dirt.'

Jessica said in a small voice, 'She warned me off, you know. She said you wouldn't be serious about me; it would all be aimed at something.'

'She wants kicking,' said Leandro dispassionately. 'Now your mother seems to fulfil the job description in an altogether more satisfactory manner.'

'*My* mother?' Jessica eyed him suspiciously. 'What do you know about my mother?'

'Just that she seems very sensible,' he said soothingly. 'At least when I spoke to her on the telephone she said that I sounded like the man her daughter was in love with and I had better come and talk to you this afternoon while she was out at the Vicarage sale of work.'

'She said that?' Jessica was shocked. 'The conniving——'

'An excellent woman,' Leandro said swiftly, kissing her. 'In marrying you I shall get a mother-in-law in a thousand. It will be worth it.'

Jessica said, 'You're marrying me for my mother?' in arctic tones.

He was laughing uncontrollably. 'Among other things.' The anorak was old and heavy and encrusted with mud, but he seemed to have very little difficulty in removing it, or the sweater underneath it. His hands slid under her shirt until they were warm against her skin. Jessica shivered and surrendered. His voice thickened. 'One or two other things. But marriage or nothing, agreed?'

She met his eyes and found them dancing with warmth and an affection so brilliant it was blinding.

'I love you,' she said softly.

His mouth curved, but he said, 'Don't change the subject. Marriage or nothing.'

His hands moved on her. She moved her shoulders voluptuously and pressed closer.

'I wasn't changing the subject,' she murmured. 'And I agree. Marriage it is.'

Pack this alongside the suntan lotion

The lazy days of summer are evoked in 4 special new romances, set in warm, sunny countries.

Stories like Kerry Allyne's **"Carpentaria Moon"**, Penny Jordan's **"A new relationship"**, Roberta Leigh's **"A racy affair"**, and Jeneth Murrey's **"Bittersweet marriage"**.

Make sure the Holiday Romance Pack is top of your holiday list this summer.

AVAILABLE IN JUNE, PRICE £4.80

Available from Boots, Martins, John Menzies, W. H. Smith, Woolworth's, and other paperback stockists.

YOU'RE INVITED TO ACCEPT **FOUR ROMANCES** AND A TOTE BAG **FREE!**

Acceptance card

| NO STAMP NEEDED | Post to: **Reader Service, FREEPOST, P.O. Box 236, Croydon, Surrey. CR9 9EL** |

Please note readers in Southern Africa write to:
Independant Book Services P.T.Y., Postbag X3010, Randburg 2125, S. Africa

YES! Please send me 4 free Mills & Boon Romances and my free tote bag – and reserve a Reader Service Subscription for me. If I decide to subscribe I shall receive 6 new Romances every month as soon as they come off the presses for £7.20 together with a FREE monthly newsletter including information on top authors and special offers, exclusively for Reader Service subscribers. There are no postage and packing charges, and I understand I may cancel or suspend my subscription at any time. If I decide not to subscribe I shall write to you within 10 days. Even if I decide not to subscribe the 4 free novels and the tote bag are mine to keep forever. I am over 18 years of age   EP20R

NAME _____

                                                          (CAPITALS PLEASE)

ADDRESS _____

_____

_____ POSTCODE _____

AND THEN HE KISSED HER...

This is the title of our new venture — an audio tape designed to help you become a successful Mills & Boon author!

In the past, those of you who asked us for advice on how to write for Mills & Boon have been supplied with brief printed guidelines. Our new tape expands on these and, by carefully chosen examples, shows you how to make your story come alive. And we think you'll enjoy listening to it.

You can still get the printed guidelines by writing to our Editorial Department. But, if you would like to have the tape, please send a cheque or postal order for £2.95 (which includes VAT and postage) to:

VAT REG. No. 232 4334 96

AND THEN HE KISSED HER...

To: Mills & Boon Reader Service, FREEPOST, P.O. Box 236, Croydon, Surrey CR9 9EL.

Please send me _____ copies of the audio tape. I enclose a cheque/postal order*, crossed and made payable to Mills & Boon Reader Service, for the sum of £_____ . *Please delete whichever is not applicable.

Signature _____

Name (BLOCK LETTERS) _____

Address _____

_____ Post Code _____

YOU MAY BE MAILED WITH OTHER OFFERS AS A RESULT OF THIS APPLICATION   ED1